MANUFACTURING
OPERATIONS MANAGEMENT

Other Related Titles from World Scientific

Service and Operations Management
by Cengiz Haksever and Barry Render
ISBN: 978-981-3209-44-2

Managing Supply Chain Operations
by Lei Lei, Leonardo DeCandia, Rosa Oppenheim and Yao Zhao
ISBN: 978-981-3108-79-0

E-Commerce Operations Management
Second Edition
by Marc J Schniederjans, Qing Cao and Jason H Triche
ISBN: 978-981-4518-62-8
ISBN: 978-981-4518-63-5 (pbk)

Hands-on Project Management: Practice your Skills with
Simulation Based Training
by Avraham Shtub and Moshe Rosenwein
ISBN: 978-981-3200-53-1

MANUFACTURING
OPERATIONS MANAGEMENT

Min-Jung Yoo
Rémy Glardon

EPFL, Switzerland

 **World Scientific**

NEW JERSEY · LONDON · SINGAPORE · BEIJING · SHANGHAI · HONG KONG · TAIPEI · CHENNAI · TOKYO

Published by

World Scientific Publishing Europe Ltd.

57 Shelton Street, Covent Garden, London WC2H 9HE

Head office: 5 Toh Tuck Link, Singapore 596224

USA office: 27 Warren Street, Suite 401-402, Hackensack, NJ 07601

Library of Congress Cataloging-in-Publication Data
Names: Yoo, Min-Jung (Engineer) author. | Glardon, Rémy, author.
Title: Manufacturing operations management / by Min-Jung Yoo (EPFL, Switzerland),
    Rémy Glardon (EPFL, Switzerland).
Description: [Hackensack?] New Jersey : World Scientific, [2018] |
    Includes bibliographical references and index.
Identifiers: LCCN 2018010671 | ISBN 9781786345332 (hc : alk. paper)
Subjects: LCSH: Manufacturing processes--Management. | Production management. |
    Operations research.
Classification: LCC TS155 .Y554 2018 | DDC 658.5--dc23
LC record available at https://lccn.loc.gov/2018010671

British Library Cataloguing-in-Publication Data
A catalogue record for this book is available from the British Library.

For any available supplementary material, please visit
http://www.worldscientific.com/worldscibooks/10.1142/Q0157#t=suppl

Desk Editors: V. Vishnu Mohan/Jennifer Brough/Koe Shi Ying

Typeset by Stallion Press
Email: enquiries@stallionpress.com

Printed in Singapore

Preface

In a time of Digitalization, Industry 4.0, the 4th Industrial Revolution, Internet of Things and Physical Internet visions, why another book on Manufacturing Operations Management? This question went of course through the mind of the authors before deciding on this endeavour.

After teaching this topic for many years to inexperienced Mater students, skilful managers and operational staff in many different industrial sectors, we gain the firm conviction that a deep understanding of the fundamentals of material and information flow management remains the key to success. Whatever the technological progresses, the new information technologies and data-management opportunities, these can only be made useful and profitable if the basics are correctly understood. The fundamental rules governing material and information flows are fundamentals that do not change; there are the basics of the so-called "Factory Physics" or "Supply Chain Physics". It is our view that the mastering of the basic principles and rules that govern these complex systems that are manufacturing organizations is a prerequisite for making significant and useful use of constant new technological developments.

Having developed over the years a specific pedagogical approach to teaching theses fundamentals, strongly inspired by colleagues all over the world with whom we shared experiences, good and bad, materials and tools, we felt that it was our duty to make our own experience available to others. We hope this work will help and support others and contribute to inspire new generations of Operations Management Students and Professionals.

Rémy Glardon and Yoo Min-Jung

Lausanne, 27 February 2018

About the Authors

Rémy Glardon is Honorary Professor of the Swiss Federal Institute of Technology at Lausanne where he founded and directed of the Laboratory for Production Management and Processes. He owns a Master in Mechanical Engineering and a PhD in Materials Science from the Swiss Federal Institute of Technology at Lausanne. After his graduate studies at EPFL, he spent several years as a postdoc at UC-Berkeley. He then moved to industry and occupied management positions in Operations and Supply Chain Management. His main interests are related to the design, configuration and strategic, tactical & operational management of value adding networks. Rémy Glardon has initiated and completed several research and consulting projects with private companies in these areas, aiming at improving the cost/performance ratio in operations management. He is the co-founder and managing partner of the consulting company Ipros.

Yoo Min-Jung is Lecturer in the School of Engineering of the Swiss Federal Institute of Technology in Lausanne (EPFL), where she teaches advanced courses in production management, simulation and optimisation technologies at the graduate level of Mechanical Engineering and Management of Technology. She received her doctorate in Computer Science — Artificial Intelligence — from the University of Paris 6. Her research domains include production and supply chain optimisation, semantic modelling and Internet of Things for product-service lifecycle management. Prior to the EPFL, she was Assistant Professor at the HEC — University of Lausanne, teaching courses at both graduate and undergraduate levels of Management Science and Business Information System.

Acknowledgements

We would like to thank Mrs. Anne Pessotto from the Nestlé group, Switzerland, and Mrs. Seong Jin Kim from Ares Trading S.A., an affiliate of Merck, Switzerland, for providing unwavering enthusiasm and valuable feedback on the manuscript. Our great appreciation goes to the students who have shared classrooms with us, from whom we could get inspiring ideas and encouragement.

The first author particularly wishes to express her gratitude to Charlie Ward for his great help with corrections and suggestions provided when he attended the Production Management course (EPFL) of the academic year 2017. The following student reviewers provided valuable feedback on the manuscript to whom I would like to oer my special thanks: John Stevenson, Jean-Nicolas Laurent Josi, Ocane Jousset, Alexandre Bouchet, and David Perone. *I have learned a lot from our discussions.*

Finally, our heartfelt thanks go to the editor and production manager of World Scientific, Mrs. Catharina Weijman and Mrs. Jennifer Brough. *Assistance provided by you was greatly appreciated.*

Yoo Min-Jung and Rémy Glardon

Contents

List of Figures

List of Tables

Chapter 1

Introduction

For any company, regardless of its size and location, their competitive business environment should be globally understood and analysed. Information and communication technology and transportation systems allow firms to purchase, manufacture, assemble, sub-contract, store, and sell their products almost anywhere. The organisation of manufacturing operations needs to be considered as a group of elements adding value to materials for customers and consumers. The value-adding elements (suppliers, machine shops, assembly factories, and so forth) compose a network in which material and information flow among them.

The extent of a Supply Chain Management (SCM) depends on the types of relation among different partners of Value-Adding Network (VAN). Taking a watch maker as a simplified example, it is likely that the watch case manufacturer would be included within the watch assembler's SCM since the business relationship between the watch assembly factory and the case manufacturer is of equal importance. The same will hold true for the case manufacturer and a precious metal supplier. The better this network performs, the more the value is created. From the point of view of global objectives, the economic welfare of each constituent is as important as the whole network's performance.

The above-mentioned reflection leads us to the following practical points:

- Each value-adding element contributing to the Value-Adding Network must be organised and managed so as to perform its tasks as efficiently as possible.

- Each value-adding element contributing to the Value-Adding Network must be organised and managed so as to contribute as much as possible to the performance of the Value-Adding Network.
- The Value-Adding Network must be organised and managed so as to deliver the best possible performance to the end customer.

Traditionally, the first point is dealt with in *Manufacturing and Operations Management*, whereas the last point is dealt with in the context of *Supply Chain Management*. In this book, we will consider the organisation and operations management of a manufacturing company as part of a Value-Adding Network. Subsequently, the Supply Chain Management itself will not be the main focus of our discussion. In other words, we will take a look at one node of the VAN and see how to organise and manage its operations to reach expected performance levels within the scope of SCM.

The internal activities of one node participating in the VAN is in general composed of procurement, value-adding operations, and distributions & sales, which are shown at the top of Fig. 1.1. This figure displays the above-mentioned example of a watch manufacturer.

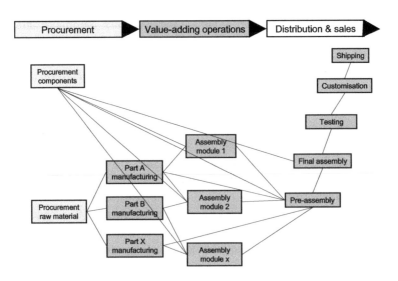

Fig. 1.1   Internal value-adding network of a node.

The core part shall be the set of value-adding operations, which includes: procurement activities to ensure the inflow of material (i.e. purchased goods) and outflow of information (i.e. purchasing order); distribution/ sales functions which in turn enable the outflow of material (delivery of goods) and the inflow of information (purchasing order of customers). The core value-adding operations then constitute recursively a network of production units as shown in Fig. 1.1.

The internal VAN has to be designed by defining what is done where, such as where the operations are executed, and where the stocks are located. Such an issue of organisation design might not be the key subject of this book. We will consider that the organisation of production systems already exists. Then, we will concentrate on how to select its appropriate management parameters and how to manage it in a changing environment.

1.1   For whom is this book written

The main purpose of this book is to introduce the essential theories and tools for production (manufacturing operations) management for students in engineering, junior professionals in supply chain and production managers who are starting their career in a manufacturing firm. With a focus on selected key techniques and a practical application of these skills, the book uses a real-world inspired case studies while providing readers with in-depth exploration. It is therefore suitable for graduates in technology management and industrial engineering, and professionals in the field of manufacturing who want to revise their practical knowledge while enhancing theoretical background.

1.2   Organisation of the book

This book discusses the following subjects with the help of a realistic case study.

Chapter 2. Basic concepts and definitions

Cost, *time*, and *flows* are the three key concepts of manufacturing operations management. The objective of this introductory chapter is to get readers acquainted with the key concepts and help understand the way how these notions are used in manufacturing operations.

Sections 1–3 introduce elementary notions and definitions of cost, production structure, and product structure. In Section 4, the typological classification of production systems is presented in a simplified and non-exhaustive way.

Chapter 3. Demand management and forecasting

The main purpose of a company is to serve its market and fulfil the demands of its customers as well as consumers. Therefore, knowing this demand is essential for running the company. Chapter 4 presents methodologies for forecasting future demands.

The first section presents the categorisation of forecasting and data types required for demand management. Basic concepts and definitions are then introduced, which are essential for understanding the other sections of this chapter. In Section 5, the decomposition of forecasting model is detailed, which is then applied to the forecast modelling methodology in Section 6.

Chapter 4. Manufacturing operations planning

The demand forecasting provides us with the base of feasible sales planning since it is the expected operating results created from the customers' demand. The quality of customer service of a manufacturing firm depends on the availability of finished products at the right moment. The manufacturing operations planning plays a major influence on the inventory level of finished products.

In Chapter 4, we discuss level-by-level processes of manufacturing operations planning, starting from the top level of planning procedures going down to the detailed level of material requirement planning.

Chapter 5. Inventory management

The central purpose of inventory is to enable quick and reliable delivery of finished products to customers. However, the downside of inventory is its high cost. Chapter 5 illustrates the foundations of inventory management with its role in manufacturing firms.

Key vocabularies and fundamental problems are explained in Section 1. Section 2 presents cost modelling which plays an important role in inventory management. In Section 3, various inventory management methods are presented with example illustrations. Section 4 deals with the critical issues of uncertainty and how to cope with it. Section 5 presents a set of statistical models used for calculating safety stocks.

Chapter 6. Just-In-Time and KANBAN management

Chapter 6 is aiming at presenting the Just-In-Time (JIT) concept and Lean management, pull and push material flows, and the KANBAN management.

Following the basic introduction to different notions, KANBAN dimensioning is presented in order to learn how to define KANBAN management parameters under a given situation of manufacturing operations. The two last sections are dedicated to comparative discussions about the different methods of material flow management, which replaces the concluding remarks of this chapter.

1.3 How to use this book

Chapter 2 introduces main terms and definitions which will be useful with the understanding of the other chapters. Therefore, if you are new to this domain, we recommend a careful reading of Chapter 2. If you have already been working in a similar domain or have already acquired such knowledge, you can directly move to the other chapters which interest you.

Apart from the introductory chapter (Chapter 2), each chapter can be read separately according to your main interests and needs. Several chapters are nonetheless interrelated. For example, for the purpose of knowing the essential benefits and limitations related to JIT and KANBAN management, it is helpful to know the basic principles of the Inventory Management in Chapter 5 in line with the MRP mechanism which is introduced in Chapter 4 Manufacturing Operations Planning.

1.4 Short introduction to our coaching sessions

"Coaching" is the name of our project class which is guided by a "coach". Rather than calling it an exercise class, we prefer calling it a coaching session since the students try to solve the required issues by their own, but with the help of guideline of their coaches. It is a project based class in which students participate in groups of 4 following a case study of a realistic firm's manufacturing operations management.

The book deals with the main subjects that students learn and practice during one semester following the same order of topic presentation and facing the same depth of reflexion. Similarly to the fact that the book deals with the case study of MotionTech or others, when the course starts, the students choose their model company, an existing company's existing products which are suggested by coaches. They then try to assimilate similar issues and answers with respect to their case study company.

The preparation of coaching sessions requires a huge amount of efforts to generate company data. Here are some of examples: determination of the company and products; definition of a fictive (simplified) bill of materials, generation of 3-year sales records with seasonality & trend; creation of productivity data in operations with cost structure and bill of operations. In Appendix A.3, we present two letters from our former coaches in order to share their experience and memories.

From the students' side as well, the course accompanied by such a project requires an endeavouring follow-up. In general, one big topic (per chapter starting from Chapter 3) is studied during around 4 weeks for the purpose of acquiring the whole content. Therefore, our course schedule is organised according to a regular sub program composed of the following points:

- First week: thematic introduction (only classroom);
- Second week: introduction to a more advanced notion (classroom, 2h) + first coaching (in group, 2h);
- Third week: introduction to a more advanced notion (classroom, 2h) + intermediary presentation in coaching (2h);
- Fourth week: final in-depth subject and outlook (classroom, 2h) + final sum-up coaching (2h);
- Finally, students submit their chapter report so as to consolidate their learning outcomes.

At the end of each chapter, we present our coaching assignment as an example, hoping that it might be somehow helpful to other instructors who are interested in organisation a project-based learning program of a similar type.

Chapter 2

Basic Concepts and Definitions

Cost, time and flows are three key concepts which constitute the central elements of production management. This chapter introduces selected concepts and definitions that are fundamental in understanding the management of manufacturing operations, while illustrating them within a realistic context as far as possible. Sections 1–3 introduce some elementary notions and definitions about cost, production structure, and product structure. The selection of terms is restricted to items required in dealing with production and operations management. In Section 4, the typological classification of production systems is presented in a simplified and non-exhaustive way. The purpose here is to familiarise the reader with important concepts such as lead-time and market synchronisation.

2.1 Cost structure

It is obvious that costs play a major role in managing a manufacturing enterprise. Getting clear insights into the definition and classification of costs, according to their nature and objective, will help understand the remaining part of this chapter without confusion. Before entering into details, let us talk about the difference between the 'cost' and 'price'. When I, one of the authors, asked this question in the classroom, interesting reactions from the students were produced. Some students thought that both are similar concepts in meaning; some of them were thinking it might be slightly different but being wondering how they were different.

Cost versus price

A cost is (according to Business Dictionary) an amount that has to be paid or given up in order to get something. In manufacturing, cost has its importance as a monetary valuation of effort, material, resources, time and utilities used, or even risks incurred. A price is the value that is put to a product or service. Price is the result of a complex set of calculations, research, understanding and risk taking ability. To summarise, price is a 'measure of value' that a product can be exchanged for, whereas cost is a 'measure of effort' put into that product. As we will see in Section 2.2, putting in more effort (therefore increasing cost) does not always entail a considerable increase in value (not increasing price). The remaining part of this section deals with the definition of cost while categorising it from different points of view.

2.1.1 *Fixed versus variable cost*

A cost is characterised by its dependence on the production volume. If it does not vary with the production volume, it is defined as a fixed cost. On the contrary, if it depends on the production volume, it is defined as a variable cost. As an example, the set-up cost of a manufacturing operation such as the stamping of steel plates is a fixed cost as it does not depend on the volume that will be produced after the set-up is completed. The cost of stamping itself is, on the contrary, variable as it depends on the production lot size, i.e. the volume of production. This differentiation is important as it affects cost and profitability calculations. In particular, the fixed and variable costs have a different contribution to the unit cost, that is, the cost of a single item.

2.1.2 *Direct versus indirect cost*

A further distinction can be made on the basis of the relation of the considered cost to a given operation or activity. If the considered cost can be directly and fully attributed to a given operation, the cost is said to be a direct cost. Labour and direct materials such as components and raw materials, which are used in manufacturing a specific product, constitute the majority of direct costs. Salaries can be direct as well as indirect cost.

If the considered cost cannot be directly or fully attributed to a given operation, but requires some calculation such as a distribution rule, then the cost is defined as an indirect cost. These costs, sometimes referred to as overhead costs, include cost for materials and supplies needed for the company's operations, such as cleaning supplies, utilities, office equipment rental, and desktop computers.

The distinction between both types of cost does not follow a clean-cut rule and depends on the main activity of the enterprise. An example could be electricity: the cost of electricity usage can be either direct or indirect cost. Electricity usage may increase with production, which is clear with the case of pulp industries. A huge amount of electricity is required for heating and cooling during the operations, which is dependent on the production volume. But in general cases, the manufacturing complex still requires a certain amount of power to maintain itself.

Table 2.1 illustrates some examples of direct and indirect costs.

Table 2.1   Direct versus indirect costs.

	Direct	Indirect
raw materials	√	
maintenance, cleaning		√
machine depreciation		√
buildings		√
management		√
administration, IT-related cost		√
energy (for heating buildings)		√
production staff	√	

2.1.3   *Hourly rate*

The Cambridge dictionary defines the hourly rate as the amount of money that is charged, paid, or earned for every hour worked. Subsequently, the production hourly rate is defined by the total production cost paid for the total production hour (or the quotient of the total cost by the total operation duration). It is linked to the performance and profitability measurement of a value-adding activity, which constitutes a central notion of manufacturing effectiveness. The hourly rate can be defined at any level of aggregation such as for a single machine or a complete workshop. In many situations, the total production time also includes non-productive times, which should be excluded from the calculation. Therefore, the production hours to be considered are equal to the effective productive time, not to the total production time.

Figure 2.1 shows how the hourly rate evolves with the production volume. If the production system is highly automated, cost is dominated by the amortisation of the highly automated equipment, which is a fixed cost. In such a case, increasing the production volume will lead to dividing an almost constant total cost by an increasing number of production hours, thereby sharply reducing the hourly rate. In contrast, if production is essentially manual, the dominating cost is variable, such as the salaries of the employees, and varies linearly with the production volume. In this case, increasing the production volume does not lead to a reduction of the hourly rate, which is almost independent of the production volume.

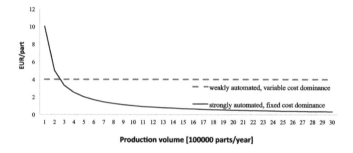

Fig. 2.1   Evolution of the hourly rate with the production volume.

2.1.4   *Cash flow and income statement*

Cash flow

The Business Dictionary defines the cash flow as incomings and outgoings of cash, representing the operating activities of an organisation. In accounting, cash flow is the difference in amount of cash available at the beginning of a period (opening balance) and the amount at the end of that period (closing balance). It is called positive if the closing balance is higher than the opening balance, otherwise called negative. Increase in cash flow can stem from: selling more goods, selling an asset, reducing cost, or increasing the selling price, for instance. It is an important concept in accounting and enterprise management since the cash flow implicitly represents the company's financial state of health. Cash flows are classified as operating, investing and financing activities. Cash flows from operating activities include cash activities related to net income, which are detailed below.

Income statement

The income statement, or statement of financial performance, measures a company's financial performance, such as revenues, expenses, profits or losses over a specific time period. In general the income statement of a company is composed of the following key elements:

- Revenue
    - (i) Sales
    - (ii) Costs of sales (direct materials costs, direct labour costs such as salaries of production workers)

- Operating incomes and expenses
    - (i) General and administrative expenses
    - (ii) Sales and marketing incomes and expenses
    - (iii) Depreciation/Amortisation expenses
    - (iv) R&D expenses

- Non-operating incomes and expenses
    - (i) Other gains (exceptional products)
    - (ii) Other expenses: foreign exchange loss, for example
    - (iii) Finance costs or income: interest expenses

Let us take a look at the definition of amortisation and depreciation. In accounting, they refer to two aspects of same concepts: the decrease in value of assets; the allocation of the cost of assets to periods in which the assets are used. If an asset is expected to produce benefits in future periods, some of these costs must be deferred based on the cost of asset, estimated useful life, residual value, etc.

The income statement is the most common financial statement which shows a company's revenue, total expenses, and also includes non-cash accounting such as depreciation, and profit or loss. A cash flow statement shows exactly how much money a company has received and how much it has spent. Subsequently, it is used to determine the short-term viability and liquidity of a company, especially its capacity to fulfil payment in terms of bills and vendors. Therefore, in order to understand how well a company invests in new technologies or what the financial capability and potential in the near future will be, it is advised to take both aspects into consideration.

For example, Tables 2.2 and 2.3 show a pharmaceutical company's income statement and cash flow statement from operating activities in 2016.

Table 2.2   Example of the income statement of a pharmaceutical group.

Revenue (Year)		2016	
	Total revenue	39,807,000	(a)
	Cost of revenue	13,891,000	(b)
Gross margin		25,916,000	(c) = (a) − (b)
Operating expenses			
	Research development	10,124,000	
	Selling general and administrative	9,762,000	
	Other expenses	651,000	
Total operating expenses		20,537,000	(d)
Operating income		5,379,000	(e) = (c) − (d)
Other expenses		720,000	(f)
Earning Before Interest and Taxes (EBITA)		4,659,000	(e) − (f)
Interest expense		−	
Income Before Tax		4,659,000	(g)
Income Tax Expense		718,000	(h)
Net Income (from continuing operations)		3,941,000	(g) − (h)

Table 2.3   Example of the cash flow of the same pharmaceutical group.

Fiscal year is January–December (EUR).

Net Income	3,941,000	(a)
Depreciation, Depletion & Amortisation	5,440,000	(b)
Depreciation and Depletion	1,640,000	
Amortisation of intangible assets	3,800,000	
Deferred income, Tax payable	1,520,000	(c)
Other funds	5,120,000	(d)
Cash Flow	12,981,000	(a) + (b) − (c) + (d)

In particular, from the point of view of production management, cash flows and income statement of a company can be referenced in the following situations: (i) Internal strategic decision: when a new product is to be launched, in order to estimate the cost and return of investment. In such a case, investment in R&D, production equipment, continuous education, new technology, as well as acquisitions must be at least partly financed internally. Establishing a corresponding net cash flow statement, before execution, will provide a first glance at the feasibility of such investment. (ii) When a company is evaluating supplier companies' performance and financial state of health before establishing a long-term contract of procurement.

The operating cash flow level is better evaluated as a relative ratio of its absolute value to the sales figures. The required level to assure a good financial condition depends on the type of enterprise. In a low-tech company, few resources are required for investment in new technology and product development. On the contrary, heavy investments are required to finance the continuous technological development in high-tech companies. Thus, cash flow below 10% may be acceptable for some enterprises whereas values above 20% may be required for others.

2.2 Production structure

The major objective of a production system is to add value to raw materials, components, sub-assemblies or finished products. Anything other than a value-adding activity is to be prohibited or at least minimised since it will not add any value but certainly add cost and time. In this subsection, the main types of production flows and production data management is described.

2.2.1 *Key types of production activities*

Any production system can be seen as a series of activities. To make it clear, let us look at the example of the micro-motor and consider the manufacturing of the stator tube only. The required activities are illustrated in Figs. 2.1 and 2.3. Among the four types of activity — manufacturing operation, transfer, transaction and stocking — only the manufacturing operation adds value to the material. All the others are not adding any value, but are modifying the location, the administrative status or nothing at all for the stocking activity. Any activities which are not value-adding operations should be restricted as much as possible.

The initial value of the raw material, in our example the low carbon steel tubes, is successively increased by each of the value adding manufacturing operations. In between these manufacturing operations, the value remains unchanged, but the cost increases due to the cost of transportation as well

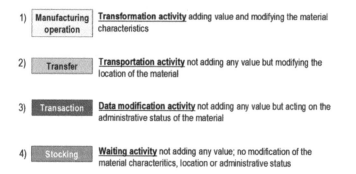

Fig. 2.2   Types of manufacturing activities — legend.

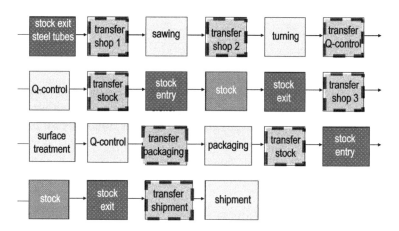

Fig. 2.3   Sequence of activities for the manufacturing of the stator tube for a micromotor.

as the cost of stocking. Figure 2.4 schematically shows the evolution of the value and cost for the production of the micro-motor stator tube.

2.2.2   *Definition of item, work in progress, and stock*

In order to efficiently manage a value adding chain, it is necessary to have precise information about the identification of the material within the production system and about its value. It is easy to keep track of identification outside a production centre, in which the material has a stable status since no transformation is in progress. On the contrary, it is difficult to keep track of such an identity within a production centre since the material is

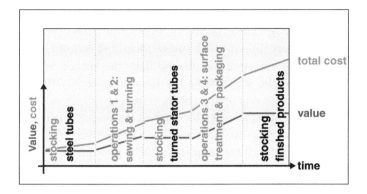

Fig. 2.4   Evolution of value and cost for the production of the stator tube.

undergoing continuous changes as a result of value-adding processes. The material is physically modified and the value is increased. The status is consequently also in progress. Any raw material, part, sub-assembly, or finished product that can be clearly identified is called an *item*. This is a general term that gives no information about the nature of the item. An item is uniquely defined by an item number as well as all the detailed description related to it.

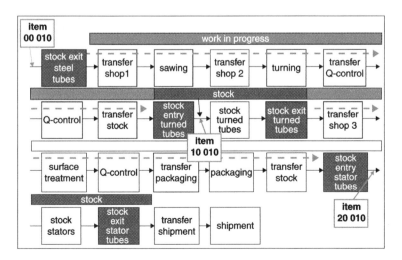

Fig. 2.5   Item, work in progress (WIP) and stock example of stator tube for micro-motor.

During a value adding process, in which a unique identification is not possible, the item is assigned the status 'work in progress' (WIP). As illustrated in Fig. 2.5, any item in stock can be identified with an item number. The steel tube has the item number 00 010, the turned tube the item number 10 010 and the stator tube the item number 20 010. A production process starts with one or several given items (00 010), adds value to it through a transformation or assembly process (sawing + turning) and gives birth to an end item (10 010) with another identification and value. Since it is difficult to track the total number of WIPs, its value is often estimated from the average between the value of the start item (00 010) and that of the end item (10 010).

Figure 2.6 provides a more generic description of items and WIP in an assembly process. In this case, the three start items 12'001, 12'002 and 14'003 are assembled into the single end item 20'001.

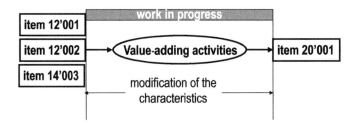

Fig. 2.6   Work in progress.

Between the various value adding processes, the items can stay within the production process. This is the case when they are moved quickly from one production centre to the next, for example, in Fig. 2.5 between the sawing and the turning workshops. But often, instead of being moved directly to the next production centre, an item can be stored in a stock or inventory, as for the turned tubes and the stator tubes. A stock can be physically separated from the production floor or integrated into it, as will be seen in Chapter 5. Here we care only about the status of the items and not about their physical location. An item in stock is identified by its item number and its location. Such information is used to calculate the total value of the stock, i.e. the sum of the values of all items in stock. As will be discussed in Chapter 5, this is essential information for determining the inventory carrying cost and estimating stock volume.

2.2.3   *Classification of items*

It is a common fact that most enterprises deal with a large number of items, often more than several 10'000. Managing such a volume of data is no easy task, which consumes valuable resources. Since the amount of resources is limited, companies prefer investing time and money only when it produces the best return on investment. It is often observed that each of the many thousands of items does not have the same importance for the company. Some items might be more significant than others in terms of their associated margin, with respect to their sales volume or marketing strategies. Whatever the reason for their particular importance, it is wise to manage the limited resources so as to allocate a larger part to key items.

Consequently, a kind of classification must first be undertaken. This section provides a basic introduction to the item classification and a brief description of the procedure of ABC classification which is one of the most used methods. The main objective of an item classification is to categorise materials or items in order to apply global management to the categorised group of items. Considering the classification criteria, various ways of classification are available. They can be of an economical as well as a technical nature, as illustrated in Table 2.4.

Table 2.4   Example of economic and technological classifications.

Classification according to economic criteria	Classification according to other criteria
Market demand in value [c.u.]	Membership of the Bill of Material of a product, product family
Requirement in volume [parts]	Base material
Value in inventory [c.u.]	Manufacturing process
Volume in inventory [parts]	Geometry
Inventory turnover ratio	Dimensions
Replenishment lead-time [d]	
Production lead-time [d]	

c.u.: currency unit, d: day.

Furthermore, classification can be done in an absolute or in a relative way depending on the objective. For example, a finished product inventory value of 500'000 EUR does not mean much without considering the company's annual sales volume. If the company sells 250'000 EUR of this product a year, the inventory level is huge since it represents 2 years of sales. On the contrary, if the considered company has a sales volume of

4'000'000/year, the above-mentioned inventory volume corresponds to 1.5 months of sales, which could be less significant than the former case. As this example illustrates, it is often necessary to use a relative ranking in classifying items. Table 2.5 provides several examples of absolute and relative classifications.

Table 2.5   Example of absolute and relative classifications.

	Absolute classification	Relative classification
Items with production lead-time	<10 days	<40% average
	from 10 to 20 days	from 40% to 60% average
	>20 days	>60% average
Items with inventory value	<10 Kc.u.	>1 month of average requirement
	from 10 to 100 Kc.u.	from 1 to 3 months of average requirement
	>100 Kc.u.	>3 months of average requirement
Items with the required volume	<1 Kpart/year	<50% of the previous planning period
	from 1 to 10 Kpart/year	from 50% to 90% of the previous planning period
	>10 Kpart/year	>90% of the previous planning period
Others		<5% of total sales volume

2.2.4   ABC classification

In business, it is often observed that a large part of the effects (typically 80%) comes from a small part of the causes (typically 20%). This is known as the 80-20 rule or the Pareto principle. For example, it is common to find that 20% of the finished product items contribute to 80% of the sales turnover or that 80% of quality problems are due to 20% of the items. This general observation forms the basic principle of the ABC classification which aims at grouping items in three categories according to their decreasing importance: A, B, and C classes. Usually the three classes are defined according to the following criteria:

- A-class accounts for the first 80% of the effect;
- B-class accounts for the next 15% (i.e. 80 to 95%) of the effect;
- C-class accounts for the last 5% (i.e. 95 to 100%) of the effect.

Figure 2.7 provides the example of the purchasing turnover analysis of a manufacturing company.

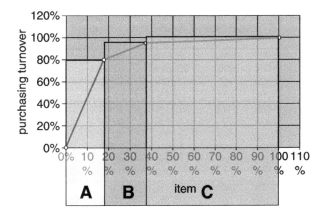

Fig. 2.7 ABC analysis of the purchasing turnover of a manufacturing company.

To perform an ABC classification, the following procedure should be used:

(1) Create a table listing each item and its corresponding effect;
(2) Calculate the sum of the effects of all items;
(3) Determine the percentage value of the effect of each item (divide the absolute value of the effect by the sum of all the effects);
(4) Rank the whole table in the decreasing order of the percentage effect (decreasing relative contribution);
(5) Determine the cumulative percentage effect, keeping the previous ranking unchanged;
(6) Plot the curve of the cumulative effect as a function of the cumulative number of items;
(7) Determine the A-class as the group of items leading to 80% of the cumulative effect (y-axis);
(8) Determine the B-class as the group of items leading to the next 15% of the cumulative effect (80 to 95% on the y-axis);
(9) Determine the C-class as the group of items leading to the last 5% of the cumulative effect (95 to 100% on the y-axis).

Figure 2.8 shows a simplified example of an ABC classification. The ABC classification is an important and powerful tool in enterprise management and particularly in operations management. It allows the selective allocation of resources according to priorities.

item	volume in inventory	% volume in inventory	cumulative % volume in inventory	class
1003	1000	38.73%	38.73%	A
1004	600	23.24%	61.97%	A
1002	300	11.62%	73.59%	A
1001	200	7.75%	81.33%	A
1005	100	3.87%	85.21%	B
1015	77	2.98%	88.19%	B
1013	56	2.17%	90.36%	B
1008	40	1.55%	91.91%	B
1011	36	1.39%	93.30%	B
1009	35	1.36%	94.66%	B
1014	34	1.32%	95.97%	C
1010	24	0.93%	96.90%	C
1016	23	0.89%	97.79%	C
1012	13	0.50%	98.30%	C
1017	11	0.43%	98.72%	C
1006	10	0.39%	99.11%	C
1021	7	0.27%	99.38%	C
1020	6	0.23%	99.61%	C
1007	5	0.19%	99.81%	C
1019	5	0.19%	100.00%	C
sum	2582			

Fig. 2.8   Simplified example of ABC analysis.

2.3   Product structure

Most finished products and sub-assemblies are made out of more than one constituting item (modules and/or single parts). For example, the electrical motor shown in Fig. 2.9 requires sub parts (simplified description):

- one rotor: the rotor is itself constituted of:
  - one shaft;
  - one torque transmission disk;
  - two bearings;
  - one retaining collar;
  - one coil.
- one stator.
- one collector cup.

This simplified example illustrates the fact that a product (or a sub-assembly) usually requires a defined number of items (from just a few for a ballpoint pen to millions for an airplane) to be produced and that they

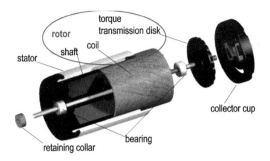

Fig. 2.9   Product structure of a motor.

must be grouped according to a structure defined during the product design. This structure is called the Bill of Material (BoM). There are many ways to represent a BoM, depending on the purpose of utilisation. In production and operations management, a hierarchical representation is often used, which is shown in Fig. 2.10 for the electrical motor.

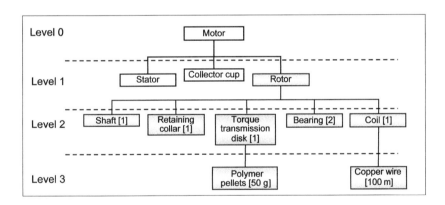

Fig. 2.10   Partial Bill of Material of the micro-motor with its four levels.

The BoM specifies the relations between the constitutive items as well as their quantities. In the previous figure it can be observed that the rotor is composed of 1 shaft, 1 retaining collar, 1 torque transmission disk, 2 bearings and 1 coil. The coil itself requires $100\,m$ of copper wire to be manufactured while the torque transmission disk needs $50\,g$ of polymer pellets. A BoM can have several levels that are numbered starting with the finished product at level 0. The partial BoM of Fig. 2.10 has 4 levels.

2.4   Production typology and market strategy

Defining classes of production helps in many ways to understand how they can be operated. In particular, their identification is a prerequisite for the purpose of choosing appropriate management methods of a manufacturing organisation. However, it is also important to understand that each enterprise is unique and continually evolving. Therefore no ideal and prevailing solution might be easily found for a specific organisation. Among various criteria of classification, in this subsection, we selectively present three of them:

- Material flow;
- Market synchronisation;
- Product structure.

2.4.1   *Material flow criterion*

A preliminary distinction shall be made between a continuous flow processes (like an oil refinery or wood pulp manufacturing) and processes leading to the outflow of discrete parts (like a pacemaker manufacturer). In this book, continuous processes will not be considered and we will concentrate on the classification of discrete part manufacturing. The discrete part manufacturing can be divided into three main categories as illustrated in Fig. 2.11:

- Mass production;
- Batch production;
- Job-shop production.

Mass production

The mass production is the production or manufacture of goods in large quantities of standardised products, frequently by assembly line of machinery. This production type deals with processing large numbers of similar products efficiently.

Job-shop

Job-shops are typically small manufacturing systems that handle small to medium-size customer orders. Production processes move on to different

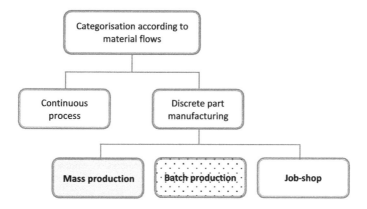

Fig. 2.11   Classification according to the type of material flow.

jobs (possibly with different customers) when each job is completed. Specialised machines are aggregate in shops by the nature of skills and technological processes. Some examples of such jobs are machining shop, grinding, or gear manufacturing, for instance.

Batch production

In batch production, components or products are produced in groups, i.e. batches, going through a series of workshops.

The rough positioning of these three production types relative to product variety, production volume and flexibility, standardisation level, and worker's proficiency is represented in Figs. 2.12 and 2.13.

The physical flow of material on the shop floor, i.e. the factory layout, also depends on the production type. Although there are no strict rules, some general trends can be learned from practical operations. In order to get insights into it, let us assume two different product families, A and B. The production routing (sequence of operations) of both product families are defined as shown in Fig. 2.14.

If we have to deal with mass production, the layout will call for two linear physical material flows. A specific production infrastructure for each product family is required while installing two optimised production lines, as shown in Fig. 2.15.

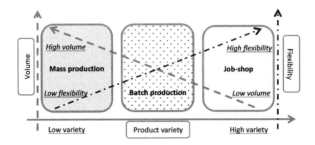

Fig. 2.12   Position regarding the product variety, production volume, and flexibility.

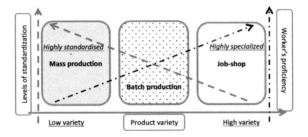

Fig. 2.13   Positioning according to the level of standardization and worker's proficiency.

Fig. 2.14   Production steps.

In case production is characterised by small quantities and a high product variety, the organisation would be oriented around production processes, each workshop being specialised in particular operations. This type of manufacturing is called a Job-shop. The material flow in a Job-shop layout is relatively complex since parts generally have to travel back and forth between the various shops while following production routings. Fig. 2.16 illustrates such characteristics of a job-shop manufacturing.

The intermediate case is characterised by a medium quantity production and an intermediary level of product variety. Some of the processes

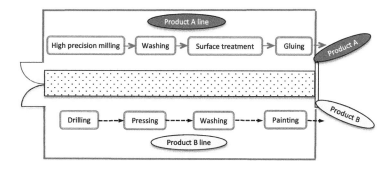

Fig. 2.15   Manufacturing floor: typical layout for mass production.

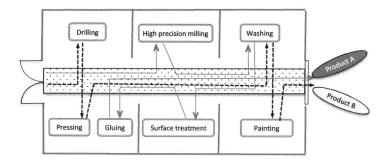

Fig. 2.16   Manufacturing floor: typical layout for job-shop production.

are specifially attributed to a given product family whereas others (particularly those requiring large investments) are shared by several product families. This organisation is therefore a mix of the two previous ones. The corresponding material flow, illustrated in Fig. 2.17, is more efficient than a Job-shop organisation but still more complex than a mass production.

Analysing an organisation's production types according to the material flow leads to interesting observations that are schematically summarised in Table 2.6.

As can be seen in Table 2.6, a Job-shop organisation type would be the most favourable one concerning the first three features (production volume, product variety, flexibility of operation), whereas for the last three criteria (level of automation, management complexity, worker's specialisation),

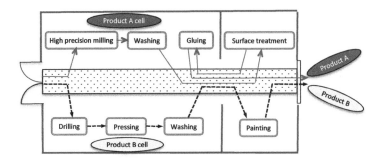

Fig. 2.17   Manufacturing floor: typical layout for batch production.

Table 2.6   Comparison of three production types.

	Mass	Batch	Job-shop
Production volume	⇑	⇌	⇓
Product variety	⇓	⇌	⇑
Flexibility of operation	not flexible	–	flexible
Break down sensitivity	⇑	⇌	⇓
Level of automation	⇑	⇌	⇓
Management complexity	low	rather high	complicate
Worker's specialisation	⇓	⇌	⇑
Lead-time	intermediate	long	very long

⇑: High or increasing.
⇓: Low or decreasing.
⇌: Intermediate level.

a mass production organisation would provide better performance. This conflicting situation shows that the current evolution of the business environment presents a real challenge to operations management and the choice of the most appropriate production organisation. Often, mixed solutions and a continuous search for improvement are the best way to face this challenge.

2.4.2   *Market synchronisation criterion*

The criterion of market synchronisation is based on two important concepts in operations management:

- The concept of acceptable delivery lead-time, T_d
- The concept of production lead-time, T_p

The acceptable delivery lead-time, T_d is the delay an average customer is ready to accept for the delivery of the product. Obviously, T_d depends on the market situation; the more ferocious the competition is, the stronger the pressure will be for a shorter delivery lead-time. T_d is also related to the product type as well as customer expectations. For a given product, an intuitive value of T_d can be expected by customers either based on experience or on the sales conditions generally offered by the competitors (1 day for a washing machine, 5 minutes for a low cost watch, 1 month for a luxury one, and so on).

It is essential to remember that:

- T_d generally decreases when market competition increases.
- T_d is laid down by the market and not determined by the enterprise.

The production lead-time T_p is the sum of the lead-times of all the processes that are required to produce and deliver the product to the customer, from component procurement to the final transportation to the customer. For the sake of simplicity, we will only consider the main categories of value adding processes, which are defined in Table 2.7 and illustrated in sequential order in Fig. 2.18.

Table 2.7 Production lead-time — main components.

Lead-time	Process	Result
T_p^p	Procurement of components, raw material	Components
T_p^m	Manufacturing of sub-assemblies	Sub-assemblies
T_p^a	Assembly of generic finished products	Generic finished products
T_p^c	Customisation of finished products	Customised finished products
T_p^s	Packaging, delivery of finished products	Delivered end products

The criterion of market synchronisation is based on the relation between T_d and T_p, i.e. between the acceptable delivery lead-time and the production lead-time. Three basic classes of production types can be identified as follows:

- $T_d/T_p > 1$: relevant to Make-To-Order (MTO)
- $T_d = T_p^s$: Make-To-Stock (MTS)
- $T_p^s < T_d < T_p$: corresponding to an intermediate case

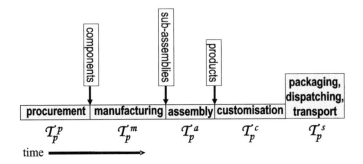

Fig. 2.18   Production lead-time: main components.

These situations are illustrated by Figs. 2.19–2.22. Particularly in intermediate cases, the downstream part of the Value Adding Chain can be managed in an MTO mode, on the basis of customer orders, whereas the upstream part shall be managed in an MTS mode, on the basis of forecasts.

Make-To-Order (MTO) situation

In the Make-To-Order situation, the production is launched after customer approval, and following characteristics are observed.

- Low inventory levels;
- Low obsolescence risk;
- Fit to the market.

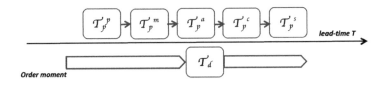

Fig. 2.19   Lead-time in the MTO situation.

The MTO type production exhibits, on the contrary, the following downfalls.

- Production load is irregular due to the demand following strategy;
- The manufacturing firm is vulnerable to technical risks.

Make-To-Stock (MTS) situation

In the situation of Make-To-Stock, the production is launched on forecasts without waiting for a specific customer order. The MTS type production provides the following advantages.

- Possibility to smooth out the production load;
- Possibility to cover a certain range of technical risk.

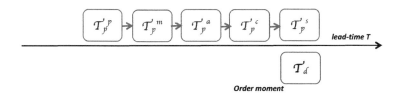

Fig. 2.20   Lead-time in the MTS situation.

However, the MTS manufacturing environment has the following disadvantages.

- High inventory levels in general;
- High obsolescence risks;
- The manufacturing is not directly connected to the market.

Intermediate situation

Intermediate situations are characterised by:

- Finished products customisation to order;
- Assembly of sub-assemblies in stock to order;
- Production and assembly of specific parts to order.

From a strategic point of view, reducing lead times can be one of the major objectives to achieve. To meet such an objective, it is important to structure the most appropriate material & information flow. However, other improvement is still necessary taking the whole production lifecycle into consideration, e.g. design for manufacturing, assembly, as well as logistics.

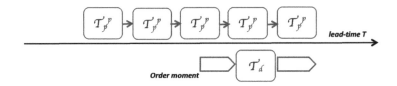

Fig. 2.21   Intermediate case 1 — Assemble-To-Order.

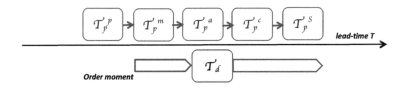

Fig. 2.22   Intermediate case 2 — Manufacture-To-Order.

2.4.3   *Product structure criterion*

The product structure criterion is based on the form of the hierarchical BoM and four basic product structure types can be distinguished:

- Converging, A-structure;
- Diverging, V-structure;
- Parallel, H-structure;
- Intermediate, X or Y-structure.

The Converging, A-structure is characterised by:

- Few finished products;
- Limited utilisation of common sub-assemblies;
- Many components/raw materials.

Assembly of printed circuit boards is a typical example.

The Diverging, V-structure is characterised by:

- Many finished products;
- Significant utilisation of common sub-assemblies;
- Few components/raw materials.

Metallurgical, paper, textile, and chemical industries are typical examples.

The Parallel, H-structure is characterised by:

- Number of finished products, sub-assemblies and components close to each other;
- Few common sub-assemblies.

Typical examples would be surface treatment, chemical cleaning, and translation services.

The Intermediate, X or Y-structure, is characterised by:

- Many finished products;
- Strong utilisation of common sub-assemblies;
- Many components, raw materials.

The automotive industry is a typical example.

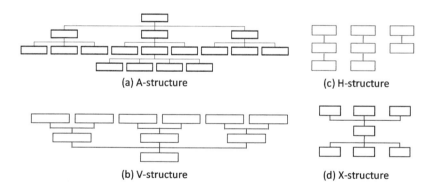

Fig. 2.23   Product structures.

2.4.4   *Production typology: Summary*

It is obvious that manufacturing operations should be differently performed depending on the product structure, material flows, location and management of inventories, and so forth. Therefore, the production types of a manufacturing firm should be analysed from different point of views so that the result of analysis should be useful with choosing appropriate operations management and methods.

2.5   Chapter summary and suggested coaching subject

In this section, we discussed the basic notions and definitions related to the cost, product, and production. The business environment which surrounds manufacturing firms is also introduced. The following subsections present example assignments at the end of this chapter.

2.5.1   *Report on enterprise description*

Objectives and tasks

The main objective of this work is to get acquainted with the enterprise you are going to analyse during the semester.

Collect and synthesise as much information as possible about the enterprise, in particular, but not exclusively about:

- Its history and qualitative as well as quantitative development;
- Its products according to technology and commercial categories;
- The localisation of its production plants, of its suppliers and of its markets;
- Its main competitors;
- The challenges the company is currently faced with or will face during the next 5 years.

Describe the main characteristics of the production by providing the following information:

- Main material and information flows of the enterprise Value Adding Network (VAN).
- Hierarchical description of the Bill of Material (BoM) of the considered product category.

Chapter 3

Demand Management and Forecasting

The main purpose of a company is to serve its market and fulfil the demands of its customers and consumers. Therefore, knowing this demand is essential for running the company. Depending on the type of business, the demand must be known, or at least estimated, before it effectively materialises into firm orders. This chapter presents methodologies of forecasting expected future demands. In a company, the forecasting serves as a basis for decision-making on strategic, tactical as well as operational levels. It is relatively difficult to elaborate reliable forecasts, particularly on a long-term horizon. This dilemma is partly covered in this chapter and will be discussed further in Chapter 4.

3.1 Introduction

Before getting into details on the importance of demand planning and fore-casting, this section presents the categorisation of forecasting and data types required for demand managements. The demand management and forecasting requires a tight collaboration between different departments of a company, most importantly among the supply chain, sales & marketing, and finance. In the following subsections, the connections between demand management and the other functions in the company such as supply man-agement and production planning, as well as the relationship between lead times and demand forecasting will be described.

3.1.1 *Types of forecast according to the aggregation level*

Demand forecasts provide valuable inputs in decision-making which takes various horizons into account (short, medium, and long term). Forecasts can be established at different aggregation levels, for example:

- For each product/customer level;
- For each single product;
- For each product type;
- For a larger product group such as a product family;
- For the total turnover of the company.

Both the forecast horizon and the forecast aggregation level depend on the use of forecasted data. Generally, the following situations occur, as illustrated in Fig. 3.1.

- Short-term forecasts at a detail level are used for short term planning and execution;
- Medium-term forecasts at an average aggregation level are used for medium term planning (general planning);
- Long-term forecasts at a high level of aggregation are used for long term planning (strategic planning).

Fig. 3.1 Relation between forecasting horizon and level of aggregation.

It is worth mentioning that the forecast horizon also depends on the product category. For example, considering the food industries, according to the product category (e.g. the chilled products versus the shelf-stable products), the short term can be hours or days whereas the medium terms can be weeks or months.

3.1.2 Forecast horizon

Forecasts are essential for making decisions at various management levels. The more a company seeks to reduce the impact of unexpected events, the more effort it must put into improving forecasts. Furthermore, due to the interconnectivity of departments and sectors in modern organisations, the beneficial effects of forecast quality will spread over the entire organisation. Forecasts play an important role in each range of decision horizon:

- Short-term operations management: Companies' operational decisions are often based on short-term demand forecasts in order to ensure the availability of resources, both human and machine. For the purpose of achieving a high level of service quality at minimum cost, accurate demand forecasting plays an important role.
- Medium-term resource acquisition: Demand forecasts are also useful during medium-term planning which involves the acquisition of resources and modification of the workforce. Depending on the type of industry, planning decisions can be made over periods from a few weeks up to several months.
- Long-term strategy of the company: Each organisation must make decisions regarding its strategic options over a long term. Some examples of such decisions include technical choices, financial and property investments, marketing actions, and development of new products. Long-term forecasts help managers improve decisions by reducing the associated risk.

Considering the 'detailed forecasting' for a 'long-term strategic planning', it is difficult to achieve a high-quality forecast. As for the zone corresponding to the 'high level aggregation' and 'short-term horizon', even though the forecasting result can provide a good quality provision, it has no benefit for execution level operations. Accordingly, the most useful combination of forecasting horizon and aggregation level goes from the lower left to the upper right corner of Fig. 3.1. Such a situation explains that forecasts of medium quality might be generally applicable.

3.1.3 Types of data

Forecasting requires raw data, which can be of different nature and come from various sources (Fig. 3.2). Some data can result from personal experience, prospective estimation or intuition such as human judgement. These data are categorised as subjective data. The time series data and related techniques will be presented in Section 3.3.

The time series data, which can be obtained from company's historical data, may be divided into the sub categories of intrinsic and extrinsic data depending on the sources of information. For example, the monthly sales of the considered product family can be categorised as intrinsic data. On the other hand, demographic data of a market can be categorised as extrinsic data. Figure 3.2 illustrates the types of data categories.

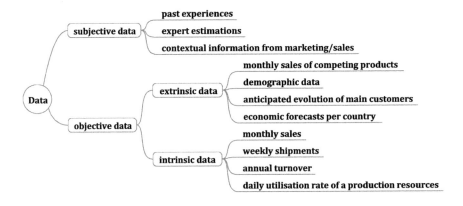

Fig. 3.2   Types of data used in forecasting.

3.1.4   *Main categories of forecasting methods*

The forecasting methods can be categorised in relation to the nature of raw data to be used. The following three forecasting methods are identifiable:

(i)   direct statistical method;
(ii) indirect statistical method;
(iii) prospective method.

Direct statistical forecasting methods often require intrinsic time series whereas indirect statistical methods are applied to forecasting based on extrinsic time series. Prospective methods cover the forecasting approaches using human judgement (personal experience, expert judgement, contextual information, etc.). The relative importance of each category of forecasting methods is roughly illustrated on Fig. 3.3 as a function of the forecast time horizon.

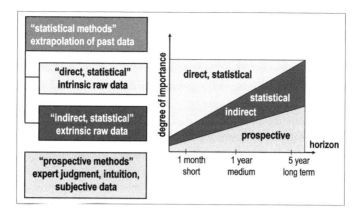

Fig. 3.3   Category of forecasting methods.

3.2   Role and importance of forecasting in supply chain management

Demand is defined as the need for a particular product or component in the marketplace. Demand management encompasses all activities required to link the market to a company, ensuring that all sources of demand are taken into account in production management activities. Demand management involves demand forecasting, order entries, quoted delivery times, customer order services, after-market demand, and so on. Demand management is strongly connected externally to the marketplace or the source of the demand. Internally, it is closely tied with the manufacturing planning and control (MPC) system. If the value-adding activities of the company cannot be accomplished within the quoted delivery lead-time, then there is a need to forecast the demand at the appropriate level of detail, prior to other MPC activities. In other words, if the production lead-time is longer than the expected (or acceptable) delivery lead-time, then the enterprise needs to rely on forecasts to produce in advance, before that actual demand materialises.

In a Make-To-Stock (MTS) situation in which all value adding activities are operated according to forecasts, detailed forecasts are required for production management. In contrast, in a Make-To-Order (MTO) environment, forecasts are less essential for managing production, although they may be necessary for purchasing. Long-term forecasts are nevertheless necessary to define a long-term strategy.

In an intermediate situation such as Assemble-To-Order (ATO), detailed forecasts are required to manage the upstream part of the value adding chain (in particular procurement, part manufacturing and production of sub-assemblies), whereas the downstream part of final assembly is run on the basis of customer orders. If the procurement lead time is longer than the production lead time, a good quality of forecasting on the upstream of the chain is important for providing a high-quality service on the downstream supply chain. Long-term forecasts are again necessary for a long-term strategy. The following sections describe the demand management function in three companies having different production organisations: Make-To-Order (MTO), Assemble-To-Order (ATO), and Make-To-Stock (MTS).

3.2.1   *Demand management in an MTO company*

Nigolava is a company specialised in the design and production of amusement park installations, such as roller coasters. Their products are designed and built according to customer specifications and must satisfy strict safety constraints. Consequently, products are mostly engineered using state-of-the-art manufacturing techniques and high performance materials. One can assume that all their products are different and require a year or more to produce. A large part of this lead-time consists of order processing, design engineering and procurement. The approach *Nigolava* has chosen to manage customer orders and to schedule production is based on the creation of an imaginary Bill of Materials (BoM) for the major sub-assemblies of the finished product. The BoM is established on the basis of the company's experience with similar projects. It includes all lead-times required to produce the different sub-assemblies (sum of the engineering design, procurement and manufacturing lead-times). Once it is established, it is processed using standard Material Resource Planning (MRP) system, which is a specialised resource planning tool that we will deal with in Chapter 4. This procedure is used for mid-term planning and helps to assure that all components, raw materials and sub-assemblies are available on time. It also supports the establishment of a mid-term capacity requirement profile for each work centre. *Nigolava* also creates long-term forecasts related to the number of contracts they expect to win (opportunities related with forth coming funfairs or carnivals) as well as the size of the projects. These long term forecasts help them plan their resource requirements (machine acquisition, hiring of research and development engineers, etc.) for the upcoming few years.

3.2.2   *Demand management in an ATO company*

Stabiviol produces packaging machines. *Stabiviol* has developed five different families of packaging machines with a wide range of options which leads to a large number of finished product combinations. Since the produced machines are huge and expensive, it is unreasonable to keep an inventory of finished products. The production is articulated around two distinct management modes.

- The replenishment of raw materials and components, as well as the production of the common sub-assemblies follows a push production system, which is consistent with MRP logic.
- The final assembly and customisation processes are pulled by the customer, which is referred to as MTO.

The production management of this ATO organisation is illustrated in Fig. 3.4. ATO environment requires both a Final Assembly Schedule (FAS) and a Master Production Schedule (MPS), which is introduced in Chapter 4: Production Planning. Rough capacity requirements for the final assembly and for component and sub-assembly manufacturing are established during the long-term planning process while respecting maximum resource capacity available within the company. The replenishment of raw materials as well as the manufacturing of components and sub-assemblies are controlled by demands and calculated using MRP logic. In this management type, the upstream part is directly dependant on the mid-term planning data included in the MPS. Both mid-term and long-term planning for product families are based on forecasts since the production lead-times of components and sub-assemblies are greater than the promised delivery lead-time to the customer.

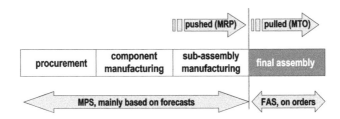

Fig. 3.4   Assemble-To-Order type manufacturing.

3.2.3   Demand management in an MTS company

Ginivik produces 30 different types of lawn mowers categorised into 3 families depending on their size and type of use. The products are differentiated by their type of body, blade and motorisation. *Ginivik* also offers different mulching kit options that can be added to the basic models.

Demand is highly seasonal but *Ginivik* has stabilised the workload in the manufacturing plant by accepting a certain level of fluctuation in the finished products inventory in agreement with the distribution centres. The competitive market requires *Ginivik* to guarantee high quality products with short delivery lead-times. *Giniviks* production follows a Make-To-Stock approach, and Just-In-Time[1] policies are used to produce common sub-assemblies. Customer orders are fulfilled from the finished product inventory held by the company distribution division. The Master Production Schedule[2] is created from forecasts of finished product families whereas the final assembly plan requires a particular modelling mechanism. Instead of establishing individual product forecasts, the model evaluates percentages from the aggregated forecasts for product families. This technique has been adopted since, during the past years, *Ginivik* has observed that the ratio of its product mix remains constant over time.

3.2.4   Importance of forecasting in supply chain management

For a large majority of companies, the delivery lead-time of finished products are greater than what the market is likely to accept, thus making it impossible to completely adopt an MTO production policy. Consequently, demand forecasting represents a key input for the survival and success of the company. In fact, demand forecasts condition the optimisation of the value-adding chain, regardless of the organisation type, level of flexibility, or reactivity. The knowledge of future demand is useful information which plays an important role in companies' decision-making at various levels in the supply chain. For the purchasing department, two types of information are essential for defining the optimal procurement policy:

• The estimated future needs (i.e. forecasted demands) in components and raw materials;
• The reliability of the forecasts.

---

[1] Just-In-Time will be discussed in Chapter 6.
[2] Master Production Schedule will be introduced in Chapter 4.

This information is important in determining the minimal coverage of needs for a specific horizon and the level of safety stock. During the process of production planning, demand forecasting contributes to making key decisions such as make or buy, in creating the Master Production Schedule from which other production stems, or in determining the required resources.

For distribution planning, forecasts provides input for dimensionning inventories and transportation capacities. Although these examples are not exhaustive, it is clear that forecasts are crucial in the global optimisation of value adding chains.

3.3 Basic concepts and definitions

This section introduces several concepts and definitions that are essential for forecasting.

Direct statistical forecasting (see Section 3.1.4) consists of extrapolating past data that have a time reference; a month, a week, an hour, a second, and so on. The collection of data with a time reference is called a time series. In the following subsection, time series and basic statistics are discussed.

3.3.1 *Time series and statistical analyses*

A time series is a collection of sequential values observed at equally spaced time intervals. For example, the monthly sold quantities, the weekly number of air plane passengers, and the yearly profits are all time series. The study of time series models can be useful in the following circumstances. Firstly, it helps obtain an understanding of the underlying forces and structure that produced the observed data. Secondly, time series analysis is essential for forecasting, monitoring or feedback and feedforward control.

Statistical forecasting consists of estimating how the sequence of past observations in a time series will continue into the future. The following list shows basic statistics.

- Mean: the usual average value;
- Median: the middle observation;
- Range: the difference between the largest and the smallest values;
- Variance;
- Standard deviation;
- Coefficient of variation.

Let us consider a time series $Y_t = \{Y_1, Y_2, \ldots, Y_n\}$ given that Y_i is the value, or observation, and $i, \ldots, n$ is the time reference at equally spaced time intervals. The mean is given by:

$$\bar{Y}_t = \frac{1}{n}(Y_1 + Y_2 + \cdots + Y_n)$$

The median is the middle observation when all the observations of the series are arranged sequentially in either increasing or decreasing order. Subsequently, in order to find the median, the observed values should be re-arranged in sequential order. In statistics, the median is the value that separates the highest half of the sample from the lowest half. Given that an increasingly ordered sequence within which $Y_i \geq Y_{i-1}$, the median is defined as follows:

$$\tilde{x} = Y_{(N+1)/2} \quad \text{if } N \text{ is odd} \tag{3.1}$$

$$\tilde{x} = \frac{1}{2}(Y_{N/2} + Y_{1+N/2}) \quad \text{if } N \text{ is even} \tag{3.2}$$

That means, if there is an even number of observations, take the mean of the two middle values.

The variance is defined as follows:

$$\sigma_Y^2 = \frac{\sum_{i=1}^n (Y_i - \bar{Y})^2}{n-1} \tag{3.3}$$

The standard deviation is simply the square root of the variance, and is defined by:

$$\sigma_Y = \sqrt{\frac{\sum_{i=1}^n (Y_i - \bar{Y})^2}{n-1}} \tag{3.4}$$

In probability and statistics, the standard deviation is the most commonly used measure of statistical dispersion. It provides a measure of dispersion that has the following properties: (1) a non-negative number; (2) having the same units as the data.

The variance and the standard deviation are measures of absolute variability in the data of the time series. The coefficient of variation (CV) is a relative measure of this variability and is defined as the ratio of the standard deviation to the mean.

The coefficient of variation is defined by:

$$CV_Y = \frac{\sigma_Y}{\bar{Y}} \tag{3.5}$$

It also provides qualitative information on the difficulty in establishing reliable statistical forecasts. The greater the value of CV, the more the data are scattered, which makes it more difficult to obtain reliable forecasts. Generally, a CV value greater than one implicitly indicates a non-trivial dataset and complicate to represent a model.

Characteristics of a time series such as seasonality can result in high CV values, however numerous methods can still be used to analyse these data which will be explained in Section 3.6.

3.3.2 *Autocorrelation analysis*

The correlation coefficients are parameters that measure the extent of the linear relationship between two variables. The autocorrelation coefficients are the correlation coefficients between two values of the same data series but separated by a fixed time lag k.

Autocorrelation plots are formed by:

- Horizontal axis: time lag k $(k = 1, 2, 3, \ldots, N)$
- Vertical axis: Autocorrelation coefficient: $r_k = \frac{C_k}{C_0}$ where C_k is the auto-covariance function defined as follows:

$$C_k = \frac{1}{N} \sum_{t=1}^{N-k} (Y_t - \bar{Y})(Y_{t+k} - \bar{Y})$$

C_0 is the variance function defined as follows:

$$C_0 = \frac{\sum_{t=1}^{N} \left(Y_t - \bar{Y}\right)^2}{N}$$

Subsequently, the autocorrelation coefficient at time lag k, for a series of N values, can be summarised as follows:

$$r_k = \frac{\sum_{t=1}^{N-k} (Y_t - \bar{Y})(Y_{t+k} - \bar{Y})}{\sum_{t=1}^{N} \left(Y_t - \bar{Y}\right)^2} \tag{3.6}$$

The series of autocorrelations for a time series at lags $1, 2, \ldots$ is called the autocorrelation function (ACF). The above-presented formula is the commonly accepted ACF function for N reasonably large with the overall mean $\bar{Y}$. In case N is large enough, the difference between summations of

$(N - k)$ and N can be ignored and the ACF values are bound between -1 and 1, inclusive.

However, when the observed data size, N, is not far greater than the potential lag value of seasonal cycle, the ACF can decrease significantly due to the increase of k value. Such a phenomenon is observed when we apply ACF to the past 3 years sales historical data ($N = 36$ months) for the purpose of detecting yearly seasonal characteristics (12 month cycle). In order to prevent a sharp decrease, ACF can also be defined as the following form:

$$r_k = \frac{\sum_{t=1}^{N-k} (Y_t - \bar{Y})(Y_{t+k} - \bar{Y})}{\sum_{t=1}^{N-k} (Y_t - \bar{Y})^2} \tag{3.7}$$

A plot of the ACF against the time lag is known as the correlogram. ACF can be used for several purposes. Firstly, autocorrelation plots are a commonly-used tool for checking randomness in a data set. For a random series, lagged values of the series are uncorrelated and we expect that $r \cong 0$. ACF can be used also to identify the presence and length of seasonality and to determine whether the data of a given time series is stationary. For instance, Fig. 3.5 represents the ACF of domestic energy consumption data which shows a strong seasonal pattern exhibited by higher ACF values at $k = 24$ and $k = 48$. If the time measure was taken every hour, such a result means a daily repetitive pattern, i.e. the peaks and the dips tend to be 24 hours apart.

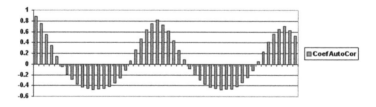

Fig. 3.5   ACF of the domestic energy consumption time series.

The ACF is also useful to check whether there is a remaining pattern in the errors after a forecasting model has been applied. Generally we consider the model to be adequate when all the autocorrelations are inferior to $\pm \frac{2}{\sqrt{n}}$ where n is the number of observations taken into account in the ACF. This test only indicates that there is no remaining pattern in the forecast errors but does not provide any particular information on the accuracy of the forecast itself.

3.3.3 *Abnormal values*

Before conducting any statistical analysis of a time series, it is necessary to check whether it contains any unusual or accidental observations. These abnormal values are often observed in the gross market segment. For instance, an advertising campaign could cause an abnormal increase in demand whereas a strike from transportation companies could cause an abnormal decrease in demand. Outliers can also result from data entry errors and are often found in industrial databases. Other additional examples that can distort the actual data include price increase/decrease, cannibalisation of one product by another one, repeated demand from customers in case of out of stock situation, and so forth. Different methods may be used to detect such abnormal values, but none of them can be applied to all cases. One possible method consists in verifying if the time series values belong to a certain confidence interval given by:

$$CI = \bar{Y} \pm 1.96\sigma_Y \tag{3.8}$$

The coefficient 1.96 corresponds to a confidence interval of 95 % for a normal distribution. Any observation of the time series, which is outside of this interval, can be considered as abnormal and is replaced for example, by the average of its neighbour values. If the time series presents a strong trend or a seasonal pattern, a confidence interval shall be evaluated for each year and each period: An observation can then be considered as abnormal if it is outside both of the yearly and of the periodic confidence interval.

An example with a quarterly time series is given in Table 3.1 where CI1 and CI2 are the lower and upper limits of the confidence interval, respectively. As can be seen, yearly CI values, as well as quarterly ones, are different ranging from Y1 to Y5 and Q1 to Q4. An observation made in Y5-Q4 with the value of 381 might not be classified as abnormal (resulting from $CI2 < 381$) since, according to the yearly CI values, this value is still within the range of CI1 and CI2 of Year 5 (<392.5).

Table 3.1   Confidence interval computation.

Quarter	Q1	Q2	Q3	Q4	Mean	σ_Y	CI1	CI2
Year 1	166	196	83	180	156.3	43.6	70.8	241.7
Year 2	169	203	97	196	166.3	41.9	84.0	248.5
Year 3	195	205	99	215	178.5	46.4	87.5	269.5
Year 4	230	243	121	263	214.3	55.1	106.2	322.3
Year 5	296	307	123	266	248.0	73.7	103.5	392.5
Mean	211.2	230.8	104.6	224.0				
σ_Y	48.2	41.5	15.3	34.9				
CI1	116.7	149.5	74.7	155.6				
CI2	305.7	312.1	134.5	292.4				

3.4   Mathematical forecasting methods

This section presents two mathematical forecasting methods:

- Moving average;
- Exponential smoothing.

3.4.1   *Moving average*

Moving-average is a technique of calculating a series of averages of data from a time series, while successively shifting the interval by the same period of time. The moving average techniques may be used for two purposes:

- For smoothing values in a time series;
- For forecasting.

Smoothing time series values consists of reducing the random fluctuation amongst a group of observations. The moving average provides a simple method for doing this. Taking the mean value of observations within a certain neighbourhood makes it possible to eliminate randomness in the data, which results in providing a reasonable estimate of that neighbourhood.

There are different ways of calculating a moving average. Here, we consider the **centred moving average**. Any original value Y_t of the time series is replaced by the average $\tilde{Y}_t$ of its symmetrical neighbouring data points. Let p be the number of neighbouring data points taken into account in the centred moving average smoothing. Then, we define the centred moving average as follows:

$$\tilde{Y}_t = \frac{1}{p} \sum_{i=t-k}^{t+k} Y_i \quad \text{with } k = \frac{p-1}{2}, \text{ if } p \text{ is odd} \tag{3.9}$$

$$\tilde{Y}_t = \frac{1}{p} \left[\sum_{i=t-k}^{t+k} Y_i + \frac{1}{2}(Y_{t-k+1} + Y_{t+k+1}) \right], \quad k = \frac{p}{2} - 1, \text{ if } p \text{ is even.} \tag{3.10}$$

Figure 3.6 illustrates the effect of the smoothing on a time series. It represents the plots of the original and the smoothed values obtained using a centred moving average with $p = 5$.

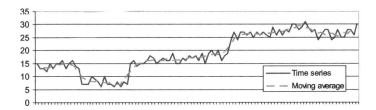

Fig. 3.6   Smoothing effect on a time series with centred moving average, $p = 5$.

Moving-average forecasting concerns averaging past demand to project a forecast for future demand, assuming that the upcoming demand pattern, at least for the next few days or weeks, is constant with random fluctuations about the average of the observed demand. Therefore, the technique calls out smoothing the random fluctuations while being sensitive to any possible changes following upcoming demands. In this case, the moving average is not centred. Let us consider p as the number of periods taken into account in the moving average, t is the current period for which the actual demand Y_i is known, and MAF_{t+1} the forecast value for period $t+1$. The moving average forecast for the period $t+1$ at the end of period t, MAF_{t+1}, can be defined as follows:

$$MAF_{t+1} = \frac{1}{p} \sum_{i=t-p+1}^{t} Y_i \tag{3.11}$$

In this forecasting model, we assume that the next value of the time series will be close to the p previous ones. Whenever a forecast is needed, the most recent past history of demand is used to compute an average value. This model is suitable for the constant or quasi-constant time series of the form $Y_t = a + e_t$ where a is constant and e_t is a random variable with a zero mean.

We can now define a **weighted moving average** by computing the moving average while assigning different weight coefficient to the series of data. In establishing forecasts with a moving average of length p, the last p observations are considered to have a similar weight in the forecasting process. In some cases, it is more appropriate to assign different weights to the previous observations, the most recent being more heavily weighted than the oldest since it will usually provide the best guide as to the future. The weighted moving average method requires p weighting coefficients so that each weighting coefficient is attributed to the corresponding p data. If one prefers to give more weight to the most recent demand and less to the older demands, the weight factors: $0.1, 0.3, 0.6$, in observation period $p = 3$ can be attributed to the computation with Y_{t-2}, Y_{t-1}, and Y_t respectively (Fig. 3.7).

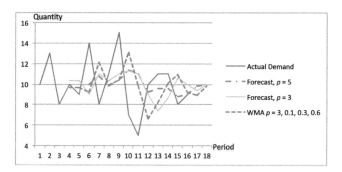

Fig. 3.7   Weighted moving average.

3.4.2   *Exponential smoothing*

The exponential smoothing follows the same basic method as the weighted moving average, but uses only one single coefficient, i.e. the smoothing constant. The forecast value for the next period with the single exponential smoothing model is:

$$F_{t+1} = F_t + \alpha(Y_t - F_t) = \alpha Y_t + (1 - \alpha)F_t \qquad (3.12)$$

where $\alpha \in [0; 1]$ is the smoothing constant.

Table 3.2 Exponential smoothing with different alpha values.

Period (wk)	1	2	3	4	5	6	7	8	9	10	11	12	13	14	15	16
Actual Demand	10	13	8	10	9	14	8	11	15	7	5	10	11	11	8	9
alpha = 0.9				10.3	10	9.1	13.5	8.55	10.8	14.6	7.76	5.28	9.53	10.85	10.98	8.30
alpha = 0.7				10.3	10.1	9.3	12.6	9.38	10.51	13.65	9.0	6.20	8.86	10.36	10.81	8.84
alpha = 0.3				10.33	10.23	9.96	11.10	10.17	10.42	11.79	10.35	8.75	9.12	9.69	10.08	9.46

Exponential smoothing advantageously requires only two records for forecasting F_t+1: the previous forecast F_t and the last known observation Y_t. An initial value for F is required in the initialising phase of the single exponential smoothing. This point will be discussed in the demand forecasting section. The development of the previous equation, listed below, demonstrates that the exponential smoothing is a kind of weighted moving average.

$$F_{t+1} = F_t + \alpha(Y_t - F_t) \tag{3.13}$$

$$F_{t+1} = \alpha Y_t + (1 - \alpha)F_t \tag{3.14}$$

$$F_t = \alpha Y_{t-1} + (1 - \alpha)F_{t-1} \tag{3.15}$$

$$F_{t-1} = \alpha Y_{t-2} + (1 - \alpha)F_{t-2} \tag{3.16}$$

$$F_{t+1} = \alpha Y_t + (1 - \alpha)[\alpha Y_{t-1} + (1 - \alpha)(\alpha Y_{t-2} + (1 - \alpha)F_{t-2}] \tag{3.17}$$

$$F_{t+1} = \alpha[Y_t + (1 - \alpha)Y_{t-1} + (1 - \alpha)^2 Y_{t-2}] + (1 - \alpha)^3 F_{t-2} \tag{3.18}$$

$$F_{t+1} = \alpha \sum_{p=0}^{\infty} (1 - \alpha)^p Y_{t-p} \tag{3.19}$$

The value of α will influence the importance of the smoothing effect.

- For $\alpha \cong 0$, the model is robust and not much dependent on an abnormal value of the last observation. It will therefore react slowly to a change in the level of the time series.
- Conversely, for $\alpha \cong 1$, the model is highly reactive to changes in recently received data.

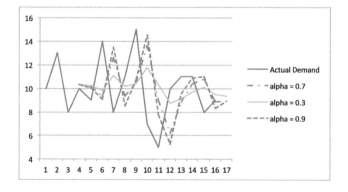

Fig. 3.8   Exponential smoothing with different coefficients.

The role of the smoothing constant is illustrated in Fig. 3.8 which shows the relative contribution of past values in the calculation of the forecast with various α values. Notice that in the previous equation, the forecast horizon concerns one period, $t+1$. It implies that, at the end of each period, a new forecast about the upcoming period is established. Forecasting over longer horizons including several periods will be dealt with in Section 3.5.

3.4.3   *Forecasting error determination*

Since the quality of forecast has impact on the quality of the decisions based on the forecast, reliability plays an important role in evaluating forecasting methods. Forecast reliability measures how well the results of the forecasting process correspond to the actual data. Despite its importance, there is no universally accepted measure of forecast error. It is recommended to understand the strengths and weaknesses of each method in a given context so as to use them relevantly and selectively. For any forecasting method, a generally accepted important criterion is honesty, or lack of bias; a given forecasting method should produce forecasts that are neither consistently high nor consistently low. To measure the bias, the mean error equation can be used. Here we describe how to calculate the mean error or other error measurements.

If Y_t is the actual value at period t and F_t is the forecasted value for this period, the forecast error, E_t, for the period t is the difference between the actual and the forecasted values:

$$E_t = Y_t - F_t \qquad (3.20)$$

Since a forecast error of e units has a completely different significance if the actual value Y was 10e units versus 100e units, a relative error measure, called percentage error PE, is defined:

$$PE_t = \frac{Y_t - F_t}{Y_t} = \frac{E_t}{Y_t} \qquad (3.21)$$

If there are actual values and forecasts over a horizon $\mathfrak{H}$ of h periods, then any error term number $n \in [1; h]$ can be considered in computing a measure of the forecast reliability. Accordingly, the following standard statistical estimators of the forecast reliability can be defined:

$$\text{Mean Error: } ME_t = \frac{1}{n} \sum_{i=t-n+1}^{t} E_i \qquad (3.22)$$

$$\text{Mean Percentage Error: } MPE_t = \frac{1}{n} \sum_{i=t-n+1}^{t} PE_i \qquad (3.23)$$

$$\text{Mean Absolute Error: } MAE_t = \frac{1}{n} \sum_{i=t-n+1}^{t} |E_i| \qquad (3.24)$$

$$\text{Mean Absolute Percentage Error: } MAPE_t = \frac{1}{n} \sum_{i=t-n+1}^{t} |PE_i| \qquad (3.25)$$

$$\text{Mean Square Error: } MSE_t = \frac{1}{n} \sum_{i=t-n+1}^{t} (E_i)^2 \qquad (3.26)$$

$$\text{Root Mean Square Error: } RMSE_t = \sqrt{\frac{1}{n} \sum_{i=t-n+1}^{t} (E_i)^2} \qquad (3.27)$$

The Mean Absolute Error, which is also known as Mean Absolute Deviation (MAD), expresses the size of the average error without considering whether it is positive or negative.

Note that in the previous equations the mean values are not centred. This is because, in forecasting, we are interested in the reliability of the n last forecasts immediately proceeding the current period. Instead of using an average calculation with a fixed number of n terms, the exponential smoothing can be used to compute smoothed average values. Assuming that actual demands are observed during the $\mathcal{H}$ horizon of total t periods, the forecast reliability of an exponential smoothing can be measured by taking the number of periods n with $\alpha \in [0; 1]$:

$$SME_t = \alpha E_t + (1 - \alpha)SME_{t-1} \qquad (3.28)$$

$$SMAE_t = \alpha|E_t| + (1 - \alpha)SMAE_{t-1} \qquad (3.29)$$

$$SMPE_t = \alpha PE_t + (1 - \alpha)SMPE_{t-1} \qquad (3.30)$$

$$SMAPE_t = \alpha|PE_t| + (1 - \alpha)SMAPE_{t-1} \qquad (3.31)$$

where:

SME_t: Smoothed mean error,
$SMAE_t$: Smoothed mean absolute error,

$SMPE_t$: Smoothed mean percentage error,
$SMAPE_t$: Smoothed mean absolute percentage error.

Table 3.3, Figs. 3.9, and 3.10 provide a simple example of the estimation of forecast reliability over the horizon $\mathcal{H}$ of 10 periods, $n = 3$, $\alpha = 0.6$.

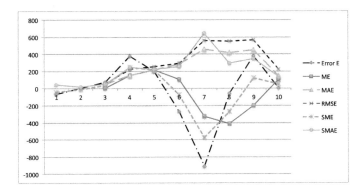

Fig. 3.9   Estimation of forecast reliability — Standard errors.

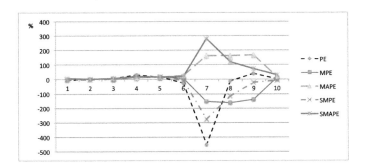

Fig. 3.10   Estimation of forecast reliability — Percentage errors.

The following arguments provide some tips on how to select an appropriate method for forecast error calculation.

• It is obvious that the result of the error calculation depends on n, the number of observations used in the data set, and α, the smoothing coefficient.
• Standard errors, such as mean error ME, SME or Root Mean Square Error RMSE, typically provide an error measure in the same units as

Manufacturing Operations Management

Table 3.3 Forecast reliability measure according to different error computations.

Period	1	2	3	4	5	6	7	8	9	10
Actual Demand	850	880	950	1300	1350	1000	200	500	900	750
Forecasted F	920	878	879	922	1149	1269	1108	563	525	750
Error E	-70	2	71	378	201	-269	-908	-63	375	0
PE	-8.2	0.2	7.5	29.1	14.9	-26.9	-454	-12.6	41.67	0
ME			1	150.3	216.7	103.3	-325.3	-413.3	-198.7	104
MPE			-0.2	12.3	17.1	5.7	-155.3	-164.5	-141.6	9.7
MAE			47.7	150.3	216.7	282.7	459.3	413.3	448.7	146
MAPE			5.3	12.3	17.1	23.6	165.3	164.5	169.4	18.1
MSE			3315	49309.7	62775.3	85215.3	312408.7	300264.7	323019.3	48198
RMSE			57.6	222.1	250.6	291.9	558.9	548	568.3	219.5
SME	-42	-15.6	36.4	241.3	217.1	-74.5	-574.6	-267.6	117.9	47.2
SMAE	42	18	49.8	246.7	219.3	249.1	644.4	295.6	343.2	137.3
SMPE	-4.9	-1.8	3.7	18.9	16.5	-9.5	-276.2	-118.0	-22.2	-8.9
SMAPE	4.9	2.1	5.3	19.6	16.8	22.8	281.5	120.2	73.1	29.2
TS	-1	-0.9	0.0	0.7	0.8	0.3	-0.3	-0.3	-0.1	-0.1
STS		-0.6	0.7	1.0	1.0	-0.3	-0.9	-0.9	0.3	0.3

the data. However, the real significance of the error is difficult to evaluate.

- The use of a Percentage Error facilitates the understanding of its significance. However, since the percentage error is defined as a ratio, problems arise in the computation of values that are zero or close to zero.

- If the sign of the error is significant (for example, non-symmetrical loss function), other error measures than the absolute error may be preferred. However, if the error sign changes regularly during the observed horizon, the calculated forecast error may be close to zero due to the compensation of positive and negative values, even though the error per period may be large (but of alternating sign).

- The use of absolute error, like the Mean Absolute Error (MAE), makes it possible to take the magnitude of errors into account including both positive and negative errors, whereas they may cancel each other out in the Mean Error (ME). However, the shortcoming of absolute errors is that they assume a symmetrical loss function, where the organisational cost of over forecasting is assumed to be the same as under forecasting and they are summed together. With these measures, the total magnitude of error is provided but the true bias or direction of the error will not be known.

- With the Mean Square Error (MSE), errors are weighted based on their magnitude in which larger errors are given more weight than smaller ones. This can be beneficial in situations where the loss function increases with the square of the error. The disadvantage of MSE is that it is inherently difficult to understand.

- The Root Mean Square Error (RMSE), which is simply the square root of MSE, may be preferred when the error is provided in the same units as the data. Like the MSE, the RMSE penalises errors with respect to their magnitude. Nevertheless, it should be noted that both MSE and RMSE are not unit-free, which makes it difficult the compare results across series.

- Outliers can distort the evaluation of forecast error. The outliers can be introduced due to a mistake in recording the data, promotional events or just random occurrences. In order to avoid unexpected results from data analysis, outliers can be filtered out before forecasting, particularly if they are due to recording mistakes. Such values can be replaced with the median, which will remove higher or lower values in favour of the middle values.

3.4.4 Tracking signal

Mathematical forecasting consists of extracting a mathematically modelled representation of the data from past time series and to use this model to compute future data. The important but implicitly given hypothesis is that the model of the past will still hold for the future; i.e. the fundamental behaviour of the system must stay the same. Consequently, it is important to have a means of checking whether this assumption is valid. Generally, it consists of computing a monitoring signal and defining critical limits between which the model is considered to remain valid. When the signal crosses a limit, the model validity must be checked and possibly revised.

A good forecasting model should produce errors that are independent and have a mean of zero. If the mean error shows a continuously positive or negative value, then the forecast is biased and the model must be re-evaluated. The tracking signal (TS) is an indicator of forecast bias and it is defined as the ratio of the mean forecast error to the absolute mean forecast error. For a forecast horizon $\mathcal{H}$ of h periods the tracking signal is defined as below:

$$TS_t = \frac{ME_t}{MAE_t} = \frac{\sum_{i=t-n+1}^{t} E_i}{\sum_{i=t-n+1}^{t} |E_i|} \quad \text{with } n \in [1; h] \tag{3.32}$$

Exponential smoothing can be applied for the evaluation of a smoothed tracking signal (STS), in order to give more weight to the most recent demand data:

$$STS_t = \frac{\delta E_t + (1 - \delta)SME_{t-1}}{\delta |E_t| + (1 - \delta)SMAE_{t-1}} \tag{3.33}$$

The tracking signal varies between -1 and $+1$. It is an indicator of forecast bias that is consistent for all observations. A tracking signal far from zero indicates that the forecasting model should be reviewed. Figure 3.11 represents the evolution of the tracking signal for the previous forecast example over a horizon $\mathcal{H}$ of 10 periods, which is also illustrated in Table 3.3.

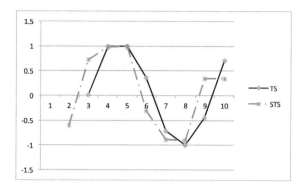

Fig. 3.11   Tracking signal (TS) and smoothed tracking signal (STS).

3.5   Demand forecasting models

This section presents demand forecasting models which are founded on the exponential smoothing.

3.5.1   *Decomposition principle*

Decomposition modelling techniques are used in time series to describe the trends and seasonal factors in the observed data. In real cases, demand varies cyclically due to seasonal effects and/or economic cycles. Usually the demand for a product or a product family can exhibit a growing trend, a stabilisation or a decreasing trend. Figure 3.12 provides an example of the historical evolution of the demand, over a horizon of 36 months, for a product family of a winter sport goods. It can be observed that the demand varies cyclically with an annual cycle (seasonality) and that it grows every year.

To generate forecasts of such a demand pattern, it is necessary to identify and describe its constitutive elements. The objective of decomposing a time series is then to isolate and model its constituting components. A time series of demands can include one or many of the following five components:

(1) The base level, $\mathcal{B}$, that provides the average volume of the demand;
(2) The trend, $\mathcal{T}$, that expresses a long-term change in the mean level, where the long-term period is a function of the model;
(3) The seasonal effect, $\mathcal{S}$, that corresponds to variations repeating at regular intervals of c periods;

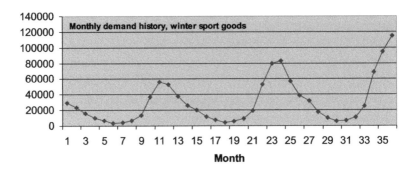

Fig. 3.12 Example of monthly demand history of a product family.

(4) A cyclic pattern, $\mathcal{C}$, apart from the seasonal variation, that may have various causes and is often found for example, in economic data such as in business cycles in the electronic or automotive industries;

(5) Random fluctuations, $\mathcal{R}$, that are any other phenomena not accounted for in the previous components and representing the unexplained stochastic variability of the demand.

For example, in the case of the previous example presented in Fig. 3.12, the following components are observed:

- A base level which shows the average volume of the demand;
- A seasonal modulation that describes how the base level is cyclically modified;
- A trend component which illustrates how the demand increases with time.

The decomposition is based on the assumption that the time series $\mathcal{Y}$ can be described by Data = Pattern + Random fluctuations, as follows:

$$\mathcal{Y} = \mathcal{F}(\mathcal{B}, \mathcal{T}, \mathcal{S}, \mathcal{C}) + \mathcal{R} \qquad (3.34)$$

In the following description, for reason of simplicity, the cyclic component will not be considered since it can be handled similarly to the seasonal component. Consequently, the decomposition model that we deal with in this chapter will be limited to:

$$\mathcal{Y} = \mathcal{F}(\mathcal{B}, \mathcal{T}, \mathcal{S}) + \mathcal{R} \qquad (3.35)$$

The mathematical formulation of the function $\mathcal{F}$ depends on the relation between the magnitude of the trend, seasonal components and the base level of the time series. If no relation exists, the components of the time series can be considered as being independent and the time series is modelled with an additive form:

$$\mathcal{Y} = \mathcal{B} + \mathcal{T} + \mathcal{S} + \mathcal{R} \qquad (3.36)$$

In contrast, if a component increases or decreases proportionally to the variation of the base level, then a multiplicative model is appropriate. Both the seasonal and trend component can be of an additive or multiplicative nature, from which nine combinations are possible as schematically illustrated in Fig. 3.13. The combinations are noted by the permutation of the two components $[\mathcal{T}; \mathcal{S}]$ with the three possible states $0, a, m$ for none, additive and multiplicative relations, respectively.

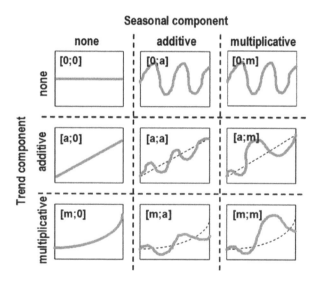

Fig. 3.13 Combination of additive/multiplicative seasonal and trend components.

Now the question is how to choose between additive and multiplicative decompositions. Although there is no straightforward rule to apply, it is often considered that:

- the additive model is useful when the seasonal variation is relatively constant over time while maintaining the same magnitude of cyclic effect across time;
- the multiplicative model is useful when the seasonal variation increases (or decreases) over time.

Multiplicative decomposition is more common with economic series. Most economic series have seasonal variations which increase with the level of the series. The most commonly found decompositions in practice are given below:

- $[a; 0]$: $\mathcal{Y} = \mathcal{B} + \mathcal{T} + \mathcal{R}$
- $[0; m]$: $\mathcal{Y} = \mathcal{B} \times \mathcal{S} + \mathcal{R}$
- $[a; m]$: $\mathcal{Y} = (\mathcal{B} + \mathcal{T})\mathcal{S} + \mathcal{R}$

The demand of the winter goods presented above is of $[a; m]$ type. Note that the random component $\mathcal{R}$ can also be described as multiplicative.

3.5.2 *Decomposition of forecasting models*

Based on the decomposition principle, several decomposition methods have been proposed. In this section, the most common cases of decomposition will be presented. When neither a trend nor a seasonal component is present, the $[0; 0]$ case, single exponential smoothing is suitable for eliminating the random component. Such a model can be described according to the following formula:

$$F_{t+1} = F_t + \alpha(Y_t - F_t) = \alpha Y_t + (1 - \alpha)F_t \qquad (3.37)$$

which implicitly means:

New forecast = last forecast + α(last forecast error), or
New forecast = α (most recent observation) + $(1 - \alpha)$ (most recent forecast)

The formula helps integrate, by choosing a relevant size of α, the weight of most recent observations to be considered.

From now on, the three most common decomposition models for forecasting are described. Each model is presented with the model equation as well as the required initial values.

$[a; 0]$ case: additive trend with no seasonality (Holt model)

For the $[a; 0]$ case (additive trend, no seasonal component), the Holt model is used. This model takes into account the presence of an additive trend component. It uses two smoothing constants α and β to estimate the base level of the time series, B_t, and its per-period trend, T_t, for a given period t. Provided that Y_t is the last observation at period t, the forecasts are established with the help of three equations, starting from estimations of the current level and applying the exponential smoothing:

$$B_t = \alpha Y_t + (1 - \alpha)(B_{t-1} + T_{t-1}) \qquad (3.38)$$

Assuming that the base level of time $t-1$ is already known, it is possible to update the estimate of the slope according to:

$$T_t = \beta(B_t - B_{t-1}) + (1 - \beta)T_{t-1} \qquad (3.39)$$

Equations (3.38) and 3.39 combine to give the following formula to generate an estimation (*forecasted value* in other words) of series h steps (periods) ahead:

$$F_{t+h} = B_t + hT_t \qquad (3.40)$$

where B_t is the current base level and T_t is the current slope (trend). Forecasting one step ahead is simply given by:

$$F_{t+1} = B_t + T_t \qquad (3.41)$$

In this model, two initial values at time t are required: the base (i.e. current) level, B, and the trend, T. One alternative is to set the initial base value to equal the most recent observation, and for the trend value to be the last observed difference, as given below:

$$B_t = Y_t \qquad (3.42)$$
$$T_t = Y_t - Y_{t-1} \qquad (3.43)$$

Another alternative for the initial trend is to set it according to a simple linear regression analysis, as:

$$T_t = \frac{Y_t - Y_{t-n}}{n} \qquad (3.44)$$

where n is the interval between any two periods, and both Y_t and Y_{t_n} are the dependent variables at time t and $t - n$.

$[0; m]$ case: no trend with multiplicative seasonality

The $[0; m]$ case is modelled by using two smoothing constants α and γ to estimate the base level of the time series and its per-period seasonal component. For a given period t, the index c signifies the seasonal cycle period, for instance, 4 for quarterly data and 12 for monthly data. The forecasting is computed given that the last observation is known as Y_t, the known seasonal coefficient is S_{t-c} at the same seasonal cyclic period with t, and the last known base level is B_{t-1}:

$$B_t = \alpha \frac{Y_t}{S_{t-3}} + (1-\alpha)B_{t-1} \tag{3.45}$$

$$S_t = \gamma \frac{Y_t}{B_t} + (1-\gamma)S_{t-c} \tag{3.46}$$

$$F_{t+h} = B_t \times S_{t+h-c} \tag{3.47}$$

The $[0; m]$ model requires two initial values: the base level B and the seasonal component S. One alternative is to set the initial values as below:

$$B_t = Y_t \tag{3.48}$$

$$S_j = \frac{Y_j}{\frac{1}{c}\sum_{i=j-c+1}^{j} Y_i} \tag{3.49}$$

where t and j are periods.

$[a; m]$ case: additive trend with multiplicative seasonality (Holt and Winters model)

The Holt model for additive trend is extended to include a multiplicative seasonality. The $[a; m]$ case model, also known as *Holt and Winters model*, is used to forecast time series with combined trend and seasonal components. The forecast requires three smoothing equations, which include three smoothing constants: α for calculating the base level of the time series, β for the trend component, and γ for the seasonal one.

$$B_t = \alpha \frac{Y_t}{S_{t-c}} + (1-\alpha)(B_{t-1} + T_{t-1}) \tag{3.50}$$

$$T_t = \beta(B_t - B_{t-1}) + (1-\beta)T_{t-1} \tag{3.51}$$

$$S_t = \gamma \frac{Y_t}{B_t} + (1-\gamma)S_{t-c} \tag{3.52}$$

$$F_{t+h} = (B_t + hT_t) \times S_{t+h-c} \tag{3.53}$$

The model initialisation requires three values:

- the base level B;
- the trend T;
- the seasonal component S.

One alternative is to set for the initial values:

$$T_t = \frac{1}{nc}[(Y_t - Y_{t-c}) + (Y_{t-1} - Y_{t-1-c})$$

$$+ \cdots + (Y_{t-n} - Y_{t-n-c})] \tag{3.54}$$

$$B_t = \frac{1}{c} \sum_{i=t-c+1}^{t} Y_i + \frac{c-1}{2} T_t \tag{3.55}$$

$$S_{t-j} = \frac{Y_{t-j}}{B_{t-j}} \text{ with } B_{t-j} = \frac{1}{c} \sum_{i=t-c+1}^{t} Y_i + \left(\frac{c}{2} - j\right) T_t \tag{3.56}$$

The seasonal coefficient of any period $t - j$ is computed on the basis of a base level B_{t-j}. The latter is computed with the average of a given cycle until time t (i.e. cycle average) and the trend value of periods $\left(\frac{c}{2} - j\right)$.

[a; a] case: additive trend & additive seasonality

Although less common in practice, the $[a; a]$ case can also be modelled using the Holt and Winters model. Three smoothing constants are required:

- α for the base level (B_t);
- β for the trend component (T_t);
- γ for the seasonal one (S_t).

This yields the following formulas:

$$B_t = \alpha (Y_t - S_{t-c}) + (1 - \alpha)(B_{t-1} + T_{t-1}) \tag{3.57}$$

$$T_t = \beta (B_t - B_{t-1}) + (1 - \beta)T_{t-1} \tag{3.58}$$

$$S_t = \gamma (Y_t - B_t) + (1 - \gamma)S_{t-c} \tag{3.59}$$

The initial values for B_t and T_t are identical to those for the multiplicative method. The seasonal components are initialised as:

$$S_{t-j} = Y_{t-j} - B_{t-j} \text{ with } B_{t-j} = \frac{1}{c} \sum_{i=t-c+1}^{t} Y_i + \left(\frac{c}{2} - j\right) T_t \tag{3.60}$$

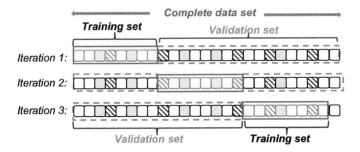

Fig. 3.14   Cross-validation technique.

3.5.3   *Model validation*

The last but not least important issue on forecasting modelling concerns model validation. Our forecasting model stems from the past historical demand data and we still do not know whether it will be generally suitable for upcoming demands. Therefore, we want to estimate how accurately our predictive model will perform in practice. Cross-validation is one of the model validation techniques for assessing how the results of a statistical analysis will generalise to an independent data set. Considering a prediction problem in a more traditional way, a model is usually given a data set of known data on which the model formulation is achieved (i.e. training), and then a dataset of unknown data is provided for the purpose of model test. The cross-validation is particularly suitable for model fitting in case there is not enough data available to partition it into separate training and test sets as in the traditional validation.

Figure 3.14 illustrates the basic idea of cross-validation. The iteration steps in cross-validation involves partitioning data into complementary subsets, (i.e. training set) on which analysis is performed, and the other subset (i.e. validation set) for testing. In general, in order to reduce variability, multiple iterations of cross-validation are performed using different partitions. In our procedure of demand forecasting, an approach similar to cross-validation will be applied to the forecast model.

3.6   Demand forecasting methodology

Forecasting demand in a real situation requires a systematic approach in order to produce reliable results in an efficient way. This section proposes a methodology to support demand forecasting on the basis of intrinsic demand data. These would be obtained in practice by extraction of an Enterprise Resource Planning (ERP) system or any enterprise warehouse data. The methods presented in this section can be applied to real situations. However, it is important to note:

- The proposed methodology should not be used blindly;
- It is recommended to use it as a support for the elaboration of an appropriate methodology related to a specific case;
- Each specific situation requires an appropriate adaptation of the proposed methodology.

The main steps and sub-procedures of the forecasting methodology are illustrated in Fig. 3.15. These are elaborated in the following subsections.

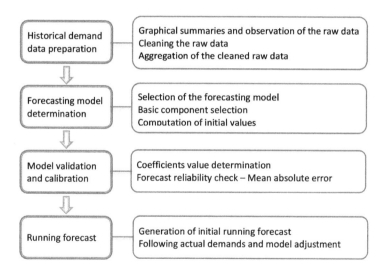

Fig. 3.15   Procedure of demand processing.

3.6.1   *Graphical summaries and observation of the raw data*

When analysing a time series, the foremost step is to plot data in graphs. Often, the basic characteristics of the data, such as patterns or any unusual information, may be quickly observed, which helps decide if deeper statistical analyses are required or not. Considering the discrete nature of time series, It is practical to use time plot charts so that trends over time, seasonal characteristics or other features can rapidly come out.

Four types of data patterns can be observed from time series:

(i) Constant or quasi-constant (horizontal);
(ii) Seasonal;
(iii) Cyclical;
(iv) Trend.

A time series is considered to be constant or quasi-constant when its values fluctuate around a constant mean. Such a series is said to be stationary in its mean. Figure 3.16 illustrates the reports from a test on 100 strikers which were consecutively produced. Since values fluctuate around a mean of about 60 units, it is considered to be constant.

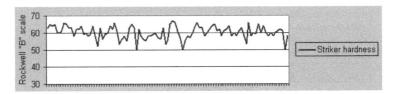

Fig. 3.16   Constant series.

A seasonal pattern is present in a time series when the values of the data vary according to a fixed time interval (a few hours, one week, one quarter, one year, etc.). For example, the domestic electricity consumption always exhibits seasonal fluctuations since the needs vary regularly in function of the time of the day, the day of the week and the season (see Fig. 3.17).

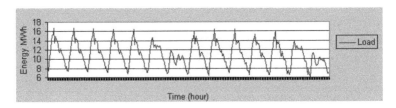

Fig. 3.17   Seasonal series: electricity consumption.

A cyclical pattern exists when the data exhibit rises and falls over a rather long interval that is not of a fixed number of periods, which is contrary to a seasonal pattern. This type of pattern is typically observed with economic series where the cycles are usually due to economic fluctuations, such as those associated with business cycles.

A time series presents a trend when there is a significantly long increase or decrease in the data. This type of pattern is common and may be found in many situations such as a plot of the turnover of a company, the gross national product, and so on.

Now, let us apply the methodology to our example case study. Figure 3.18 provides an example of the plot of raw sales data for one finished product of a winter goods producer, the WinTech company, over a 36 month time horizon.

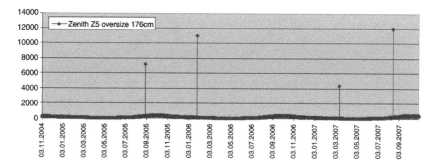

Fig. 3.18   Historic daily sales data for one finished product of WinTech.

The following observations can be made:

- The series is continuous. Sales values are present every month and most probably every week and day;
- Four unusual points (outliers) are observed, which might be due to recording errors;
- A weak seasonal effect can be observed in the form of yearly increases around September–October.

The next step is to clean the raw data by removing the outliers.

3.6.2   *Raw data cleaning*

To clean the raw data, the confidence interval approach presented in Section 3.3.3 is used. The graphical observation indicates that a first cleaning over the full horizon would be appropriate as the outliers are far apart from the main curve.

The values Y_t satisfying the following criterion

$$Y_t \geq \bar{Y} + 1.96\sigma_Y \qquad (3.61)$$

are eliminated and replaced by

$$Y_t = \frac{Y_{t+1} + Y_{t-1}}{2} \qquad (3.62)$$

The cleaned series is then plotted again and its general appearance is observed. Figure 3.19 shows the same data set for one finished product of WinTech after cleaning, i.e. replacing the four outliers.

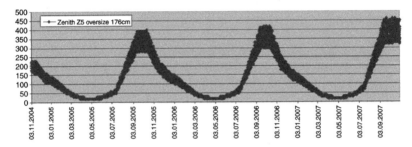

Fig. 3.19   Cleaned data of the historic daily sales of WinTech for one finished product.

The data look now much more regular and the seasonal effect is clearly visible. Its annual periodicity is confirmed which is not surprising for a winter goods producer.

3.6.3   *Aggregation of the cleaned raw data*

The data considered so far are single customer orders that are sequentially ordered according to a time scale. In a company, when forecasts are needed, it is often analysed per planning period. If the purpose of demand management is the elaboration of the production plan as the level of aggregate family, the planning period is usually a month, whereas the given data here concerns daily records. The next step then consists of aggregating the raw data per month in order to generate a new monthly time series. Figure 3.20 presents the monthly aggregate time series of the historical sales for the same finished product of the WinTech company.

For the purpose of elaborating the production plan of the company, an additional aggregation for the *product family* (Zenith Z5 oversize) may be pursued by adding all the monthly sales data of each finished product belonging to the same product family. Figure 3.21 shows the results of the family level aggregation.

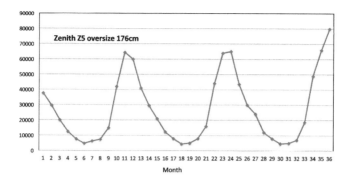

Fig. 3.20   Monthly aggregated sales data of WinTech for one finished product.

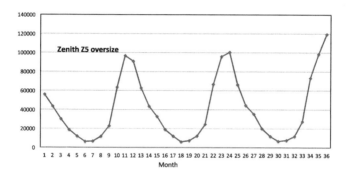

Fig. 3.21   Monthly aggregated sales data of WinTech for one product family.

We can observe the existence of a strong seasonal effect and a slight positive trend. The next step is to identify which forecasting model to apply.

3.6.4   *Determination of the forecasting model by decomposition*

This section describes how to choose an appropriate forecasting model on the basis of exponential smoothing and the decomposition principles. As seen in Section 3.5.2, a time series may be decomposed into seasonality, trend and randomness (possibly a cyclic effect as well). There is no single best procedure to analyse a time series to identify its components. The optimal procedure may depend on the relative importance of the trend versus seasonal components.

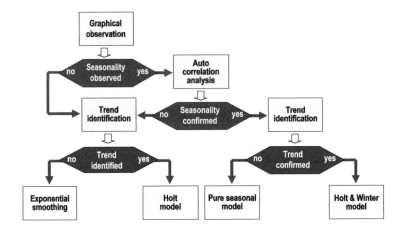

Fig. 3.22   Decision flowchart for forecasting model selection.

The first step concerns the identification of the most dominating components, such as trend or seasonal components, and removing their effect from the time series by the "de-trend" or "de-seasonal" process. Considering an additive trend decomposition, the de-trend process is achieved by subtracting the trend estimates from the series. For a multiplicative decomposition of a seasonal effect, on the other hand, this is achieved by dividing the series by the seasonal coefficients. Figure 3.22 illustrates the procedure for determining the forecasting model when a dominating seasonal component is observed. In case a dominating trend component is observed, the procedure should simply be reversed to examine the trend first.

Autocorrelation and cycle identification

In the WinTech case, the seasonal effect is easily observable with the periodicity of 12 months. However, in practice, if the seasonal characteristics are not clearly shown, a verification using autocorrelation analysis could be useful. The result of the autocorrelation for the aggregated data (Zenith Z5 oversize) is given in Fig. 3.23.

The result demonstrates the existence of a 12 month seasonal effect, which corresponds to a cycle value $c = 12$.

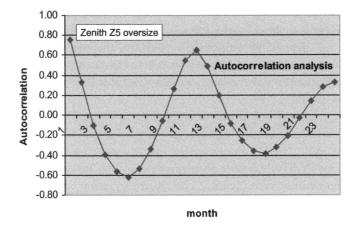

Fig. 3.23   Autocorrelogram for the Zenith Z5 aggregated data.

Trend identification by cyclic moving average and linear regression

The next step deals with the identification of a dominant trend effect. The extraction of a trend starts with smoothing the time series for the purpose of noise reduction. Two processes for trend identification are presented below. In the case of an additive trend, this can be done by:

(i) Calculating the centred moving average values, $\bar{Y}_t$:

$$\bar{Y}_t = \frac{1}{c} \sum_{i=t-(c-1)/2}^{t+(c-1)/2} Y_i \quad \text{if c is odd} \tag{3.63}$$

$$\bar{Y}_t = \frac{1}{c} \left[\sum_{i=t-(c-2)/2}^{t+(c-2)/2} Y_i + \frac{1}{2} \left(Y_{t-c/2} + Y_{t+c/2} \right) \right] \quad \text{if c is even} \tag{3.64}$$

(ii) Calculating the trend coefficient by applying linear regression analysis to the smoothed values.

Simple linear regression is a statistical method that allows to study relationships between two continuous quantitative variables:

• One variable, often denoted x, is regarded as independent variable.
• The other variable, denoted y, is regarded as the outcome, or dependent variable.

The simplest form of the equation with one dependent and one independent variable is defined by the formula $y = c + b * x$, where y = estimated outcome, i.e. dependent variable, c = constant, b = regression coefficients, i.e. the slope, and x = independent variable. Given that our example case includes 36 months' sales record, we have in total 3 cycles of 12 months. The above-presented centred moving average formula allows us to compute the average measure of any period Y_t while taking the number of period ($c = 12$) into consideration varying the range of t with $6 < t < 31$.

In Fig. 3.24, the $\bar{Y}$ values and the linear regression line are shown for the previous WinTech Zenith Z5 family. It can be concluded that the data exhibits an additive trend model. The linear regression calculation provides an initial value of the additive trend coefficient, $T' = 166 \ part/period$.

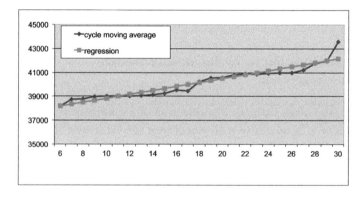

Fig. 3.24   Additive trend identification for WinTech Z5 family.

Seasonal component identification and de-seasonal process

The next step involves the identification of seasonal coefficients. If the multiplicative model is used, the seasonal coefficients can be computed by the ratio between the average value and the actual value, as illustrated in Table 3.4. The example shows that, in 2016, the total sales of 10,000 units was achieved demonstrating different amounts per period of sales.

Next year, the company is expecting an increase of 10%. Table 3.5 shows that, using the seasonal factor of each period and the expected periodic average sales, the forecasting of 2017 per period can be obtained by multiplying the factor by the expected sales of each period. Here, the set of

Table 3.4   Past sales record with computed seasonal factors.

2016 period	Past sales	Average sales	Seasonal factor
1	2,000	2,500	$2000/2500 = 0.8$
2	3,500	2,500	$3500/2500 = 1.4$
3	3,000	2,500	$3000/2500 = 1.2$
4	1,500	2,500	$1500/2500 = 0.6$
Total	10,000		

computed coefficients, $0.8, 1.4, 1.2, 0.6$, constitutes the seasonal component of the forecasting model.

Table 3.5   Forecasting for 2017 using computed seasonal factors.

Next year	Expected sales	Seasonal factor	Forecasted value
1	2750	0.8	$2750 \times 0.8 = 2200$
2	2750	1.4	$2750 \times 1.4 = 3850$
3	2750	1.2	$2750 \times 1.2 = 3330$
4	2750	0.6	$2750 \times 0.6 = 1650$
Total	11,000		

It is worth mentioning a requirement specific to forecasting with seasonal components. The forecasted periods should cover the whole cycle of a seasonal pattern, here 4 periods, not simply one period next to the current time. Subsequently, the training set is to include the full cyclic horizon for the purpose of maintaining the seasonal characteristics. During the running forecast generation using exponential smoothing, the smoothing coefficient shall be applied while taking the whole cycle into a consideration, as illustrated in Fig. 3.25.

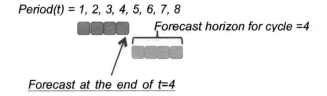

Fig. 3.25   Running forecast with seasonal effect.

In dealing with time series with cyclic effect, the seasonal component can be obtained by eliminating the seasonal effect and creating a de-seasonalised time series $\tilde{Y}_t$. A generalised equation of seasonal characteristic is developed below.

For a periodic cycle, c, defined by $\left[t^0, t^0 + (c-1)\right]$, the average of a given cycle (i.e. cycle average) should be firstly computed:

$$\bar{Y}_c = \frac{1}{c} \sum_{t=t^0}^{t^0+(c-1)} Y_t$$

Using the trend coefficient, $\tilde{Y}_t$ is computed according to the following formula:

$$\tilde{Y}_t = \bar{Y}_c + T'\left[t - t^0 - \frac{c-1}{2}\right]$$

With the WinTech example, we have three cycles from 36 months' sales record. Subsequently, the values of three cycle averages are computed. Fig. 3.26 shows the deseasonalised time series $\tilde{Y}_t$ of the WinTech Zenith Z5 family.

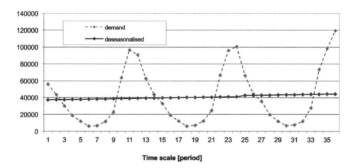

Fig. 3.26   Deseasonalised time series for WinTech Z5 family.

The initial seasonal components S'_t can then be determined by the ratio of the actual demand Y_t over the de-seasonalised one $\tilde{Y}_t$:

$$S'_t = \frac{Y_t}{\tilde{Y}_t} \tag{3.65}$$

Table 3.6 provides the values of the three sets $S(1)$, $S(2)$, $S(3)$ and the chosen initial values S' obtained by a weighted average for the WinTech Zenith Z5 family.

Table 3.6   Seasonal components for WinTech Z5 family.

weight	year 1 $S_t(1)$ 0.15	year 2 $S_t(2)$ 0.35	year 3 $S_t(3)$ 0.5	S'_t
period (t)				
1	1.50	1.60	1.55	1.56
2	1.16	1.11	1.04	1.08
3	0.80	0.83	0.83	0.82
4	0.49	0.48	0.46	0.47
5	0.31	0.30	0.27	0.29
6	0.16	0.15	0.15	0.15
7	0.17	0.18	0.18	0.18
8	0.30	0.30	0.27	0.29
9	0.59	0.60	0.62	0.61
10	1.64	1.63	1.66	1.65
11	2.48	2.34	2.22	2.30
12	2.32	2.44	2.69	2.54

3.6.5   *Model validation and calibration*

In this section, we proceed with the validation of the forecasting model. Since we have a limited size of dataset, the same set shall be used for three different purposes while partitioning them accordingly:

(a) For identifying initial trend and seasonal components in the forecast model;
(b) For the validation of model;
(c) Initialisation for future horizon.

The effective partitioning is illustrated in Fig. 3.27. The full dataset is to be used for modelling the initial forecasting decomposition. The second cycle will then be used for the model validation by comparing the generated forecasting on the cycle with the existing third cycle data.

It could be argued that using the third cycle for initialisation as well as for validation is incorrect. Although this is formally true, under the given condition, the data size is too limited to have more data for validation. In such a situation, it is preferable to use a larger partition of data for identifying the initial trend and seasonal components for the sake of model reliability, which was the resulting choice of data partition strategy.

The remaining steps are summarised below:

(1) Initialisation of forecast model for validation cycle (from $t = 25$ to 36)
(2) Generating forecast of validation cycle

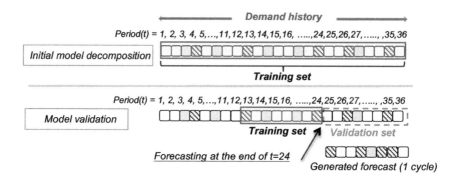

Fig. 3.27   Partitioning the time series for three purposes.

(3) Model validation on validation cycle
(4) Determination of the smoothing constants for further forecasting (after the initial one)
(5) Initialisation for future horizon (after validation cycle)

As discussed previously, in order to proceed forecasting by exponential smoothing, two types of information should be provided: the smoothing coefficients, and the initial values. With the initial trend and seasonal components being calculated, the initial base remains to be determined to obtain the final forecasting model. The initial base value depends on the period, t, which is the starting period of forecasting. In our case study which follows, the determination of a specific starting point is therefore related with the purpose of time series exploration and partitioning.

Generating forecasts of the period from $t = 25$ to 36

The corresponding situation is summarised on the lower part of Fig. 3.27, the generation of forecast at the end of $t = 24$. Here the main idea is that, before applying the exponential smoothing technique, we use the third cycle of the dataset to validate the initial model. If the obtained forecast reliability is not satisfactory, further analysis would follow.

Recall that for the [a;m] case, the forecasting model is:

$$F_{t+h} = (B_t + hT_t) \times S_{t+h-c}$$

The model initialisation for the validation cycle requires the determination of the initial value for the base B_v', which is the base value of the last period of the previous cycle. Given that the validation cycle is the third cycle, the previous cycle is cycle 2. Then, B_v' can be computed from the average value of cycle 2, $\bar{Y}_2$, and the initial trend T'.

$$B_v' = \bar{Y}_2 + \frac{c-1}{2}T'$$

In the case of the WinTech Zenith Z5.family, this gives:

$$B_v' = B_3' = B_{24} = \bar{Y}_2 + \frac{c-1}{2}T' = 40243 + 5.5 \times 166 = 41156$$

The forecast can then be fully initialised according to the [a;m] model:

$$F_{t+h}' = (B' + hT') \times S_{t+h}' \text{ with } h \in N$$

It should be pointed out that this model provides the initial forecast F' over a horizon $\mathcal{H}$. For the case of the WinTech Zenith Z5 family, the initial forecasting model for cycle 3 (validation cycle) is:

$$F_{t+h}' = (41156 + h \times 166) \times S_{t+h}'$$

The result is summarised in Table 3.7.

Measure of forecast reliability — MAPE

After determining the initial model for the validation cycle, the next step is to measure the forecast reliability. The initial forecasted values F_t' are compared to the actual historical values Y_t using the following relations so as to compute the Mean Absolute Percentage forecasting Error, $MAPE$, over the validation cycle.

$$F_{24+h}' = (41156 + h \times 166) \times S_h' \text{ with } h \in [1; 12] \tag{3.66}$$

$$MAPE = \frac{1}{12} \sum_{h=1}^{12} \left| \frac{Y_{24+h} - F_{24+h}'}{Y_{24+h}} \right| \tag{3.67}$$

The results for the WinTech Zenith Z5 family are shown in Table 3.7. As for the reliability measure and the rate of acceptance, there is no standard thread to reference. It depends on each company's strategy and the risk to management. However, from a general point of view, these results demonstrate that the model is reliable enough, that we accept the initial forecast to enhance further using exponential smoothing.

Table 3.7 Initial forecasting model validation.

t	Y_t	F'_t	APE'_t
25	66260	64456	2.7%
26	44510	44876	0.8%
27	35500	34251	3.5%
28	19840	19662	0.9%
29	11855	12150	2.5%
30	6710	6458	3.7%
31	7750	7498	3.2%
32	11920	12187	2.2%
33	27440	26056	5.0%
34	73360	70547	3.8%
35	98290	98849	0.6%
36	119500	109806	8.1%
MAPE			3.1%

3.6.6 *Identifying smoothing constants for further forecasting*

The initial forecast model developed so far allows computing a first (initial) forecast over a chosen horizon $\mathcal{H}^0 \left(t^0; t^0 + \mathcal{H}\right)$.

In a real operating situation, forecast of the following horizon $\mathcal{H}1(t^0 + 1; t^0 + 1 + \mathcal{H})$ happens as soon as the actual demand Y_{t^0+1} is known. Similarly, the following forecast $\mathcal{H}2 \left(t^0 + 2; t^0 + 2 + \mathcal{H}\right)$ will be available soon after that the actual demand Y_{t^0+2} has been known as the new forecast should be based on the previous one. The following sequence illustrates the forecast horizons progressively shifted by one period, under the assumption that the forecast horizon remains unchanged (which is not necessarily the case):

$$\mathcal{H}1(t^0 + 1; t^0 + 1 + \mathcal{H}); \mathcal{H}2(t^0 + 2; t^0 + 2 + \mathcal{H}); \ldots; \mathcal{H}n(t^0 + n; t^0 + n + \mathcal{H})$$

For all forecasts following the initial one, the model parameters B_t, T_t and S_{t+h-c} will have to be adapted using exponential smoothing, according to the following equations for the $[a; m]$ case:

$$B_t = \alpha \frac{Y_t}{S_{t-c}} + (1 - \alpha)(B_{t-1} + T_{t-1}) \tag{3.68}$$

$$T_t = \beta (B_t - B_{t-1}) + (1 - \beta)T_{t-1} \tag{3.69}$$

$$S_t = \gamma \frac{Y_t}{B_t} + (1 - \gamma)S_{t-c} \tag{3.70}$$

Since the three smoothing constants have an influence on forecast reliability, it is important to determine an optimal set of the smoothing constants α, β, and γ. Among many solutions, we suggest an algorithm which tries to find a coefficient set producing a minimal forecasting error by an iterative way.

Let $\mathcal{H}_v(t_v; t_v + (c-1))$ be the forecast horizon of the validation cycle of length c. The procedure is composed of the following steps:

(1) Initiate the forecast over a horizon $\mathcal{H}$ at a period $t_v - n$, with $n \in [3; c/2]$.
(2) Compute the initial forecast for the horizon $\mathcal{H}^o(t_v - n; t_v - n + (c-1))$ based upon the following equation: $F'_{t+h} = (B' + hT') \times S'_{t+h-c}$ with $h \in [1; c]$.
(3) Choose a set of values α_j, β_k with $\alpha, \beta \in [0; 1]$.
(4) Compute a new forecast over the horizon $\mathcal{H}_1(t_v - n + 1; t_v - n + 1 + (c-1))$ by adjusting the initial model parameters using the following relations:

$$B_t = \alpha_j \frac{Y_t}{S_{t-c}} + (1 - \alpha_j)(B_{t-1} + T_{t-1}) \tag{3.71}$$

$$T_t = \beta_k (B_t - B_{t-1}) + (1 - \beta_k)T_{t-1} \tag{3.72}$$

$$F_{t+h} = (B_t + hT_t) \times S'_{t+h-c} \tag{3.73}$$

(5) Compute the forecast error, $MAPE_1(j, k)$.
(6) Repeat steps (4) to (5) with n other horizons $\mathcal{H}_q(t_v - n + q; t_v - n + q + (c-1))$ with $q = [2; n]$.
(7) Compute the average $MAPE$ of the n forecasted horizons, $\overline{MAPE}(j, k)$.
(8) Repeat steps (3) to (7) with several other sets of values α_j and β_k in order to cover the variable space $\alpha_j, \beta_k \in [0; 1]$ with reasonable distribution.
(9) Select the set $(\alpha, \beta)_0$ that minimises $\overline{MAPE}(j, k)$ from the computation results collected so far.

The procedure is schematically illustrated in Fig. 3.28 for the specific case of $n = 4$ and $c = 12$. Note that the smoothing constant γ for the seasonal component is not taken into account in the previous procedure. Rather than varying the seasonal coefficient, it is recommended using a fixed high value (for example $\gamma=0.9$) in order to give a predominant weight to the most recent value of the seasonal components.

In the case of the WinTech Zenith Z5 family, the application of the previous procedure leads to the function $\overline{MAPE}(j, k) = f(\alpha_j, \beta_k)$ which gives an optimal set $(\alpha_0, \beta_0) = (0.1, 0.1)$ with the computed error rate

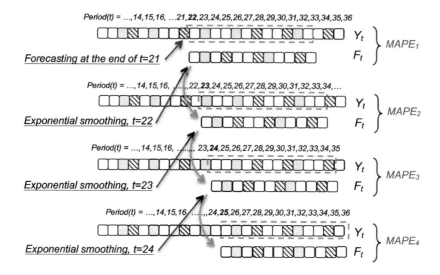

Fig. 3.28   Smoothing coefficient optimisation.

$\overline{MAPE}(j,k) = 2.73\,\%$ (Table 3.8). Finally, with the determination of the optimal values $(\alpha, \beta)_0$, the forecasting model is fully elaborated.

Table 3.8   Optimal smoothing constant determination for the WinTech Zenith Z5 family — Average $MAPE(j,k)$.

	β				
α	0.1	0.3	0.5	0.7	0.9
0.1	2.73%	2.88%	3.04%	3.23%	3.42%
0.3	3.04%	3.63%	4.23%	4.86%	5.46%
0.5	3.44%	4.42%	5.41%	6.33%	7.20%
0.7	3.86%	5.27%	6.62%	8.02%	9.73%
0.9	4.36%	6.24%	8.43%	11.10%	14.21%

3.6.7   *Running forecast generation*

Final forecast model

The final forecasting model is composed of two sub-models:

- The initialisation model for the first forecast over a horizon $\mathcal{H}$;
- The running model for all upcoming forecasts.

Using the initialisation model:

$$F'_{t+h} = (B' + hT') \times S'_{t+h-c}$$

and the running model

$$B_t = \alpha \frac{Y_t}{S_{t-c}} + (1 - \alpha)(B_{t-1} + T_{t-1})$$

$$T_t = \beta (B_t - B_{t-1}) + (1 - \beta) T_{t-1}$$

with $(\alpha, \beta) = (0.1, 0.1)$

$$F_{t+h} = (B_t + hT_t) \times S'_{t+h-c}$$

After one full cycle, S' shall be replaced by:

$$S_t = \gamma \frac{Y_t}{B_t} + (1 - \gamma) S_{t-c}$$

with $\gamma = 0.9$. The obtained results for the case of WinTech Zenith Z5 family are shown in Fig. 3.29. The third column contains the initial forecasting established at the end of $t = 36$ whereas the fourth column contains the following forecast series established at $t = 37$ (i.e. the running forecast at the end of month 37) when the actual demand is observed.

Period	Y_t	F'_t	F_t	B'_t	B_t	T'_t	T_t	Period	S'_t	S_t
25	66260									
26	44510									
27	35500									
28	19840									
29	11855									
30	6710									
31	7750									
32	11920									
33	27440									
34	73360									
35	98290									
36	119500			44492		166				
37	70000	69666			44680		168	25	1.56	
38		48410	48436					26	1.08	
39		36892	36913					27	0.82	
40		21223	21236					28	0.47	
41		13143	13152					29	0.29	
42		6823	6828					30	0.15	
43		8218	8224					31	0.18	
44		13288	13298					32	0.29	
45		28051	28075					33	0.61	
46		76151	76217					34	1.65	
47		106531	106628					35	2.30	
48		118069	118181					36	2.54	
49			73126					37		1.57

Fig. 3.29 Full data and forecasted series.

Computation examples

Initial forecast computation with the Initial model starts with the general equation:

$$F'_{t+h} = (B' + hT') \times S'_{t+h-c}$$

Computation example for F_{37} : $t = 36, h = 1 \Rightarrow$

$$F'_{37} = (B' + hT') \times S'_{25} = (44492 + 166) \times 1.56 = 69666$$

Another computation example for F_{47}: $t = 36, h = 11 \Rightarrow$

$$F'_{47} = (B' + 11 \times T') \times S'_{35} = (44492 + 11 \times 166) \times 2.30 = 106531$$

Further forecast computation with the Running model is achieved based on the general equation:

$$F_{t+h} = (B + hT) \times S'_{t+h-c}$$

Running model computation using exponential smoothing ($\alpha = 0.1; \beta = 0.1; \gamma = 0.9$)

$$B_t = \alpha \frac{Y_t}{S_{t-c}} + (1 - \alpha)(B_{t-1} + T_{t-1})$$

Future situation at $t = 37$

The main purpose of using the exponential smoothing with coefficient values is to let the forecasting model react to the forth-coming actual demands. After that the forecasting is established at $t = 36$, the real values of actual demands will be know continually receiving the sales records of the company. Let us assume that at the end of month 37 the known amount of actual demand equals 70000, which is greater than the forecasted value, $F'_{37} = 69666$. Now, the forecasting model can react to the actual value regenerating another horizon of forecast. The following computation explains how it works.

Computation example for $t = 37, \alpha = 0.1$, with the actual observation $Y_{37} = 7000$:

$$B_{37} = \alpha \frac{Y_{37}}{S_{23}} + (1 - \alpha)(B_{36} + T_{36}) = 0.1 \frac{70000}{1.56} + 0.9(44492 + 166) = 44680$$

Given that

$$T_t = \beta(B_t - B_{t-1}) + (1 - \beta)T_{t-1}$$

For $t = 37, \beta = 0.1$:

$$T_{37} = \beta\,(B_{37} - B_{36}) + (1 - \beta)\,T_{36} = 0.1\,(44680 - 44492) + 0.9 \times 166 = 168$$

Computation example for $F_{38} : t = 37, h = 1 \Rightarrow$

$$F_{38} = (B_{37} + hT_{37}) \times S'_{26} = (44680 + 168) \times 1.08 = 48436$$

Computation example for $F_{48} : t = 37, h = 11 \Rightarrow$

$$F_{48} = (B_{37} + hT_{37}) \times S'_{36} = (44680 + 11 \times 168) \times 2.54 = 118181$$

3.7 Chapter summary and coaching guideline

In this chapter, we have presented the different methods of forecasting, which are composed of several components such as base, seasonal component, trends, and randomness. In order to extract each component, different forms of mathematical or statistical tools should be appropriately used. The chapter shortly summarised basic concepts and useful formula for that purpose and then went through how to make complex forecasting model.

The following subsections present example assignments extracted from our coaching sessions.

3.7.1 *First week — Learning basic concepts*

Before starting the first coaching session, each group of students is provided with a set of sales records which concerns the case study company's past three-year business. In general, they receive the data concerning at least two product families, and two products per family.

The objectives of this coaching session are:

- To get a first (rough) understanding of the characteristics of your company's historical demand data;
- To identify the probable typology of the demand data, which will serve as a basis for further development of the forecast model.

Your tasks for this coaching session

You are asked to complete the following tasks and to be ready to present, in the coaching session, the procedure you used and the results you obtained.

- Create graphs to represent the historical demand data, observe and comment what you could learn from observation.
- Clean the historical demand data using an appropriate method; analyse and comment on the revised graphs.
- Propose a reference planning period for data aggregation and demand forecasting.
- Aggregate the cleaned data per reference planning period and per product family.
- Identify the probable demand typology for each product family (constant, cyclic, seasonal, with trend).

Preparatory discussion

Discuss the autocorrelation method with your coach if the concept is not clear since the intermediate presentation includes the autocorrelation analysis.

3.7.2   *Second week — Intermediate presentation*

The goal of this phase is to summarise the result of first analysis of the demand data, and consolidate it in a well-structured presentation.
Time slot per group: 15 min presentation, 5 min Q&A.

Your tasks for intermediary presentation

The tasks to complete and the results to obtain:

- Drawing graphs of the historical data.
- Data cleaning (abnormal values).
- Aggregation of the cleaned demand data according to the most appropriate reference planning period for the considered enterprise (week, month, quarter).
- Aggregation of the cleaned data per referenced planning period and per product family.
- Autocorrelation analysis of the aggregated data (per product family).
- Identification of the demand typology for each product family (constant, cyclic, seasonal, with trend).

Provide your data in the form of clearly documented Excel sheets. Prepare a PowerPoint presentation of your results in putting forward the most significant points (hypothesis, methods, difficulties, results).

Preparatory discussion

After the presentation, to discuss and choose an appropriate forecasting model, based on the identified demand typology. Select a preliminary forecast model according to the identified demand typology.

- Discuss or validate your idea on how to compute the possible initial trend components.
- Discuss how to compute initial seasonal components.

3.7.3 *Third week — Consolidating the whole concepts*

The objectives of this coaching session are:

- To define the initial forecast model and measure the reliability of your forecast.
- To select optimised smoothing coefficients for the running forecast model.
- To generate the forecasted demand for the next 15 months.

Your task for this coaching session

- Compute probable initial trend components.
- Compute probable initial seasonal components.
- Validate the proposed initial model and comment on the results of the validation process.
- Define optimised smoothing coefficients for the running forecasting model.
- Forecast the demand of your product families for the next 15 months.

Chapter 4

Manufacturing Operations Planning

4.1 Introduction

In Chapter 3, the forecasting method is presented so as to establish expected future demands. The demand forecasting provides us with the base of feasible sales planning since it is the expected operating results created from customer orders of the manufactured products. The quality of customer service of a manufacturing firm depends on the availability of finished products at the right moment and the manufacturing operations planning plays major influence on the inventory level of finished products.

In this chapter, we discuss level-by-level processes of manufacturing operations planning, starting from the top level of planning procedures going down to the detailed level of material requirement planning. The objective of the manufacturing operations planning can then be formulated as follows:

> Draft a plan on the basis of anticipated market needs that should assure the adequate availability of material and resources for satisfying customer's orders and support company strategy.

The subjects are organised around the following topics:

- Bill of Materials, cost and productivity data revisited
- Sales and operations planning in a manufacturing firm
- Aggregate production planning process
- Master production scheduling and techniques
- Generating Final Assembly Schedule
- Material Requirement Planning: basic tools and techniques
- Capacity plan

In general, the manufacturing operations planning should assure:

- The availability of an adequate capacity (for supply, production, and so forth).
- The availability of material (such as raw materials, components, sub-assemblies).
- A customer service level which corresponds to the company's strategy at minimum total cost.
- People management.

Figure 4.1 is a schematic presentation of the objectives of planning.

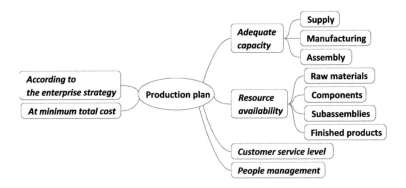

Fig. 4.1   Summary of the objectives of manufacturing operations planning.

The planning procedure is based on a hierarchical process going from a long-term aggregate level to a short-term detailed level. Here, the aggregate or detailed levels refer to not only the product structure but also the planning horizon. By proceeding level-by-level through the planning hierarchies, the above-mentioned objectives are revalidated while taking different levels of product details and considering different ranges of decision horizon. This means that long-term planning usually deals with product families or just the turnover of a business area, whereas short-term planning is usually established using data related with specific items (finished products, sub-assemblies, components, and so on).

The principle of the hierarchical planning process is schematically illustrated in Fig. 4.2.

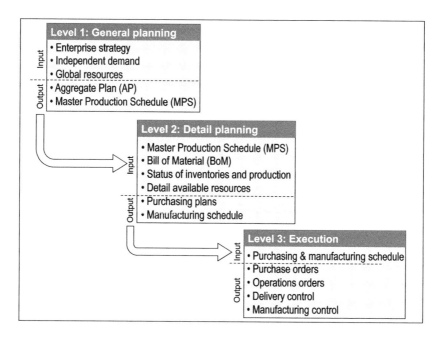

Fig. 4.2   Hierarchical manufacturing operations planning: level-by-level details.

Main elements of the general planning at level 1

The general planning at the highest level concerns the Aggregate Production Planning which establishes the overall directions of operations planning by balancing the sales plan and available production resources.

The first step consists of establishing the Aggregate Production Plan, or Aggregate Plan (AP), on the basis of the expected market demand, i.e. demand forecasting, the production strategy and the available resources. The resulting plan is established at the level of product families. Before proceeding the planning processes on a more detailed level, the feasibility of the AP at this level must be validated with regard to available aggregate resources in the firm. If required, the firm may have to revise the high level plan or adjust it so as to balance appropriately the required versus available resources.

The AP serves then as the input to the Master Production Schedule (MPS). The MPS is also based on the expected market demand and the available resources, but dealing with single finished products. This is the turning point at which the independent market demand is transformed into dependent demand managed by the firm. A similar validation of available resources against required resources must be achieved at this level.

Main elements of the planning at level 2

At this level, the planning process takes the MPS as input. This process involves often the MRP (Material Requirement Planning[1]) procedure that uses a hierarchical explosion of the demand from the finished products to the lowest level of the BoM. The feasibility of the detailed requirement plans should be validated at this level against available resources. It is worth mentioning that such a hierarchical process helps avoid potential imbalance between available versus required resources as early as possible starting the process from its aggregate level.

Main elements of the detail planning at level 3

This execution level consists of acting according to the production schedule at level 2. It should be pointed out that, depending on the production typology, the actual operating processes may vary from the initial plans; this is particularly the case for the downstream production activities that may be executed on order.

In Fig. 4.2 the example of purchasing and manufacturing control are presented at level 3.

4.1.1   *Illustration case MotionTech*

In the remaining sections of this chapter, the procedures and computations related with the planning levels 1 and 2 are presented. Each single element (procedure, computation) is simple, but the combination of different elements and the large size of data to handle, render the overall process much complex. For the sake of better understanding, each level of the planning process is illustrated with a running example: a fictive company called MotionTech, presented in Chapter 2, producing high performance ironless micro motors. Examples of MotionTech products are illustrated in Fig. 4.3.

---

[1]MRP will be discussed in Section 4.5.

Fig. 4.3   Example of MotionTech products — motor.

MotionTech product structure

A MotionTech motor is composed of three main subassemblies:

- 1 rotor (shaft, coil, torque transmission disk)
- 1 stator (steel tube & permanent magnet)
- 1 collector cup

A typical motor structure includes other additional items such as:

- 2 bearings
- 1 retaining collar

The product structure is schematically represented in Fig. 4.4.

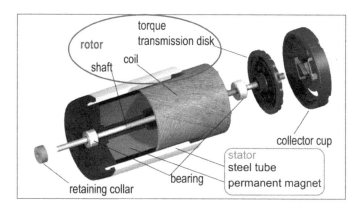

Fig. 4.4   Schematic representation of the product structure of a MotionTech motor.

A typical Bill of Material (BoM) of a MotionTech product is given in Fig. 4.5.

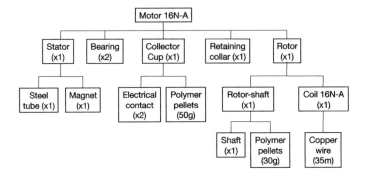

Fig. 4.5   Bill of Material (BoM) of a MotionTech product.

MotionTech buys the following components and raw materials from suppliers:

- For the rotor: shaft, insulated copper wire, polymer pellets
- For the stator: steel tube, magnet
- For the collector cup: electrical contacts, polymer pellets
- Additional items: bearings, retaining collar

Production process

The major production steps of MotionTech motors are described below according to the order of operations:

- Coils are produced by a proprietary winding and baking process. Different motor characteristics are determined by changing the winding. Therefore, there are different coils per product family (i.e. motor diameter).
- Shaft and torque transmission disk are assembled by injection moulding, using the steel shaft as an insert, to produce the rotor-shaft.
- The rotor is then put together by gluing the coil on the rotor-shaft.
- The stator is assembled by gluing the magnet inside the steel tube.
- The collector cup is produced by injection moulding, using the electrical contacts as inserts.

- Finally the motor is assembled by putting together the rotor, the stator, the bearings and the retaining collar.

The manufacturing operations are structured according to the major processes and characteristics, as shown in Fig. 4.6.

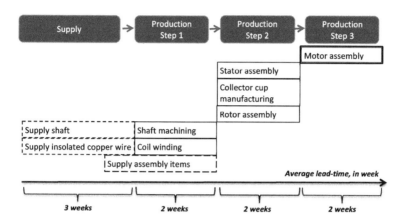

Fig. 4.6   Major production steps (Bill of Operations) of a MotionTech motor.

Productivity data and product cost structure

The cost and productivity data of the MotionTech production are given below:

- Four product families: 12N, 16N, 24N and 35N (the numbers represent the motor diameter in mm).
- High-level planning horizon: $9\,months$.
- Hourly rate of direct labour: $HR_m = 43\,c.u./h$.
- Presence time per week: $40\,h$.
- Effective production time per worker: $34\,h/week$ or $136\,h/month$.
- Average supply lead-time: $3\,weeks$.
- Average payment term to suppliers: $4\,weeks$.

For the purpose of establishing the AP with cost-related plan (such as purchasing, labour cost), rather than using the actual purchasing price, we will use the average product cost structure per product family. The rough cost structure of the four product families are given on Table 4.1. Those data will be used later for establishing a high level production planning and validating other costs.

Table 4.1   Cost structure of four product families of MotionTech motors.

Product family	12N	16N	24N	35N
Sales price (c.u.[a]), PR_s	550.00	650.00	950.00	1400.00
Material cost/sales prices, α	10.9%	10.0%	8.9%	8.6%
Direct labour cost/sales price, η	10.3%	8.7%	6.5%	4.5%

[a]c.u.: currency unit.

Using the illustrated cast study, the following section discusses how to establish the AP, which is the first step of level 1 planning.

4.2   The aggregate production plan

The Aggregate Production Planning is the highest level procedure in the context of the global planning activities which establishes the Aggregate Production Plan. The objective of this planning activity is to find an aggregate operations plan which fulfils the expected market demand at minimum cost. The aggregate plans then serve as a base for other short-term planning. The AP is characterised by the following features:

- It concerns aggregate product items in total volume; typically 5 to 15 product families;
- It covers a medium-term horizon; typically 6 to 18 months;
- It is revised regularly, often monthly, while comparing actual resource availability and the projected resource capacity;
- It can be consulted from all operations of the company for the global allocation of aggregate resources such as direct labour, machines, and purchasing.

It should be noted that the definition of a medium range planning horizon depends on the product type and market characteristics. The medium-term horizon suggested in this section considers a typical case of machine manufacturing.

Figure 4.7 describes the rough procedure of creating an AP. The previously established forecasting at the product family level can be one of the important inputs into the aggregate production planning. This step produces an initial AP, whose goal is to draft the medium-term objective of

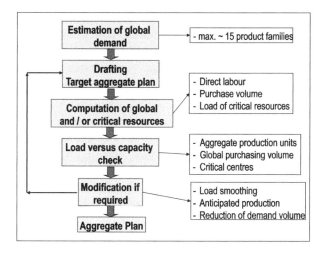

Fig. 4.7   Rough procedure for the creation of the aggregate plan.

production. On this basis, the global requirements for critical resources (the production load) are computed. The target resources can include aggregate resources such as global direct labour, as well as the financial capability for purchasing.

In the next step, the required production load is compared with the expected available capacity. In case a satisfactory adequacy is not reached, it is required to modify the AP and/or the expected available capacity. The load/capacity balance for critical resources is validated after that the AP is confirmed.

At the AP level, the important criterion of decision-making concerns the volume of total sales or the aggregate profit of the company. Therefore, the AP can be computed in currency units (*c.u.*) or in pieces (*pcs*), based on the actual purchasing price and production loads, or on the basis of the average product cost structure per product family.

The result of the AP is directly related with the inventory state of the considered finished product since the customers' demand materialises in the sales of finished products.

Planning strategies

In developing the AP, two opposite strategies can be contrasted:

- Demand following strategy, also named as pure chase strategy;
- Stable production, or level strategy.

The demand following strategy consists of adapting the production capacity so as to meet the market requirements, whereas the stable production strategy implies keeping the production loads as constant as possible.

A mixed strategy can also be chosen, which is often the case in real operations. It is a kind of hybrid planning strategy taking advantage of both extreme cases. Due to different constraints which hinder manufacturing companies from following one or the other extreme alternative, in the mixed strategy, companies accept to produce more during a slack demand period so as to be less influenced by demand fluctuations during a peak period.

Figures 4.8 and 4.9 illustrate fictive results of three alternative strategies: the two extreme ones and a mixed strategy. The demand following strategy leads to important fluctuations of the production load, but allows to produce the exact amount of products required per month, and therefore does not require any buffer inventory. With this strategy, it is possible to respond dynamically to changing market demand while running a low risk of delivery break-down. However, there are some drawbacks to this strategy: complexity in management due to the continuous modification of the production load, potential supplier relation problems, and the cost of changing production capacity.

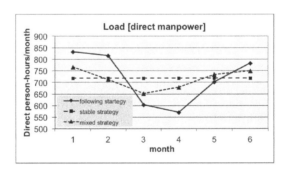

Fig. 4.8   Comparison of three production strategies — load.

If a company pursues the stable production strategy, it is relatively easy to manage its operations and supplier relations thanks to the constant production load. However, it is difficult to respond efficiently to the market changes, which often entails a delivery breakdown. In addition, a considerable amount of cost should be paid for maintaining buffer inventories.

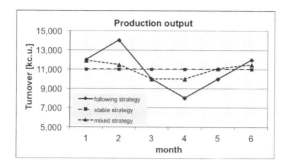

Fig. 4.9   Comparison of three production strategies — volume of products.

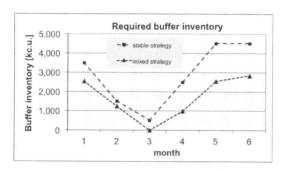

Fig. 4.10   Comparison of production strategies — buffer inventory.

Figure 4.10 shows that the average inventory equals $2833000\,c.u.$, which is equivalent to yearly inventory carrying cost of $500000\,c.u./year$.

The mixed strategy tries to compromise the extreme cases by responding to market changes, on the one hand, and seeking to reduce the delivery breakdown, on the other hand. In Fig. 4.10, the average inventory reaches $1700000\,c.u.$ (yearly estimated cost $300000\,c.u.$), which indicates a certain amount of inventory carry costs to be paid but less than the stable strategy.

In practice, a mixed strategy is often chosen as an appropriate solution to many companies' operations planning.

4.2.1   *Starting the planning process with forecasted demand: MotionTech example*

To explain the process of aggregate production planning, let us consider the MotionTech's product families. MotionTech receives monthly forecasts per product family from its subsidiaries, which have been consolidated by the company. The resultant sales forecast for the four product families is given in Table 4.2.

Table 4.2   Sales forecast of the MotionTech motor families.

Month	1	2	3	4	5	6	7	8	9
12N	2800	2850	2900	3050	3250	3350	3550	3550	3350
16N	3350	3300	3400	3600	3800	3900	4150	4150	3900
24N	1900	1800	1950	2000	2150	2250	2350	2400	2250
35N	1400	1500	1450	1550	1600	1800	1750	1800	1700
Total	9450	9450	9700	10200	10800	11200	11800	11900	11200

The monthly sales forecast may represent the expected delivery of finished products, probably to the finished goods' inventory or a distributor's warehouse, which will be consumed when real customer orders take place. A feasible AP must on the one hand assure the availability of the finished product (*meet the market demands*) and, on the other hand, be compatible with the projected available resources required for producing products (*meet the internal constraints*).

In order to meet the delivery time of finished products, the production should be achieved beforehand, which often takes several periods. Using the forecast as input, we can compute the required number of direct workers taking the production lead-time into consideration. The detailed procedure is presented in the following subsection.

4.2.2 *Defining the monthly ratio of production load*

Provided that the AP planning period is set to a month, we need to compute the monthly ratio of production load, which can span several planning periods. This step is necessary when the production lead-time is longer than the planning period. For the sake of simplicity, the method is based upon the following hypotheses:

(1) We only consider the direct labour cost and work hours as the main influencing factors on the production load;
(2) The production load is linearly distributed over the production lead-time;
(3) One month is composed of four weeks;

(4) Demands from customers are also linearly distributed, which means that if the sales of 100 products are expected in a month, the customer orders will arrive 25 products per week.

Concerning the linear load distribution, if such an assumption is not valid, other methods of computation should be used to take non-linear load distribution into account.

Month i	1				2				3	
Monthly F(i)										
Week j	1	2	3	4	5	6	7	8	9	10
Weekly PPw(j)				2					1	
Operations steps for PPw(4): 2nd week of final assembly	Production Step 2		Production Step 3							
Operations steps for PPw(9) :1st week of machining			Production Step 1		Production Step 2		Production Step 3			
Symbolic presentation of operations load			M4, 2 M9, 1							

Fig. 4.11   Production load computation (a) — case with week 4 and 9.

In Fig. 4.11, the demand forecast of month i is presented as $F(i)$, and $PPw(j)$ is the amount of finished products which should be available for each week to satisfy customer demands, where j is the week index. The weekly $PPw(j)$ can be computed by dividing the monthly amount, $F(i)$, into the number of weeks per month, 4 in this case.

In order to understand the method of production load computation, let us consider the week 3 production load with two delivery cases: a sale in week 9 requires production during the weeks 3 to 8, and the production for the delivery of week 4 should be finished in week 3.

Given that the expected amount of deliveries per week is presented as $PPw(4) = 2$ and $PPw(9) = 1$ respectively, the production load is schematically presented as follows:

- M4, 2: production load for the delivery of week 4, the volume of 2 products
- M9, 1: production load for the delivery of week 9, the volume of 1 product

By expanding the notion of load distribution in Fig. 4.11 to further planning horizon, Fig. 4.12 illustrates the production load for fulfilling the

Month i										
Monthly F(i)	8				12				4	
Week j	1	2	3	4	5	6	7	8	9	10
Weekly PPw(j)	2	2	2	2	3	3	3	3	1	1
Symbolic presentation of operations load	M2,2									
	M3,2	M3,2								
	M4,2	M4,2	M4,2							
	M5,3	M5,3	M5,3	M5,3						
	M6,3	M6,3	M6,3	M6,3	M6,3					
	M7,3	M7,3	M7,3	M7,3	M7,3	M7,3				
		M8,3	M8,3	M8,3	M8,3	M8,3	M8,3			
			M9,1	M9,1	M9,1	M9,1	M9,1	M9,1		
				M10,1	M10,1	M10,1	M10,1	M10,1	M10,1	

Fig. 4.12   Production load computation (b) — case covering three months.

deliveries from week 2 to week 10 with the integration of the monthly forecast and their weekly distributions.

(i) For each manufacturing operation, the value added during one week represents $\frac{1}{6}$ of the total required added value since the production steps are assumed to linearly add value during the 6-week production lead-time.

(ii) In week 1, production works (adds value) on the amounts to be sold in week 2 to 7 (M2 to M7).

(iii) In week 2, production adds value on the amounts to be sold in week 3 to 8 (M3 to M8).

(iv) In week 3, production adds value on the amounts to be sold in week 4 to 9 (M4 to M9).

(v) Finally in the last week of month 1, week 4, production adds value on the amounts to be sold in week 5 to 10 (M5 to M10).

Now, we would like to summarise the production load of a given month i with respect to the delivery planning of the upcoming months $i+1$, $i+2$, which allows to make the production load ratio per month. The month i's production load is selectively illustrated in Fig. 4.13.

Figure 4.13 shows that the production load of the month i should take the sales volume of three months into consideration, i.e. month i, $i+1$, and $i+2$. For the month 1 for instance, the weekly work load of week 1 to week 3 are allocated to the products to be sold during the weeks 2 to 4, each of which representing $\frac{1}{4}$ of the forecast for month 1. Similarly, the amount to be sold in each of the weeks 5 to 8 represents $\frac{1}{4}$ of forecast for month 2 and the amount to be sold in each of the weeks 9 to 12 represents $\frac{1}{4}$ of forecast for month 3. Assuming that the month 1 can be generalised and referenced to month i, and month 2 and 3 can be referenced to month

Month i		1		
Monthly F(i)		**8**		
Week j	1	2	3	4
Weekly PPw(j)	**2**	**2**	**2**	**2**
Symbolic presentation of operations load	M2, 2			
	M3, 2	M3, 2		
	M4, 2	M4, 2	M4, 2	
	M5, 3	M5, 3	M5, 3	M5, 3
	M6, 3	M6, 3	M6, 3	M6, 3
	M7, 3	M7, 3	M7, 3	M7, 3
		M8, 3	M8, 3	M8, 3
			M9, 1	M9, 1
				M10, 1

Fig. 4.13   Production load computation (c) — computing the total load of month i.

$i + 1$ and $i + 2$ for each, during the month i production adds value for:

$$6 \times \frac{1}{6} \times \frac{F(i)}{4} = \frac{6}{24} F(i) \text{ (upper-part dotted line in Fig. 4.13)} \qquad (4.1)$$

which means, $\frac{1}{6}$ for the amount of week 2, $\frac{2}{6}$ of the amount of week 3 and $\frac{3}{6}$ of the amount of week 4. Similarly regarding the forecast of month $i + 1$ and $i + 2$, month i's production adds value for:

$$15 \times \frac{1}{6} \times \frac{F(i + 1)}{4} = \frac{15}{24} F(i + 1) \text{ (middle-part line in Fig. 4.13)} \qquad (4.2)$$

$$3 \times \frac{1}{6} \times \frac{F(i + 2)}{4} = \frac{3}{24} F(i+2) \text{ (bottom-part dotted line in Fig. 4.13)} \ (4.3)$$

The final ratio is computed by combining the above-mentioned distributions, which is given below:

$$\frac{6}{24} F(i) + \frac{15}{24} F(i + 1) + \frac{3}{24} F(i + 2) \qquad (4.4)$$

From now on, Eq. (4.4) will be used as basis for the computation of other values.

4.2.3   *Computing direct labour distribution*

Given that the coefficient β is the amount of direct labour per product, Eq. (4.4) is applied to computing the production load, PL, in person-hours, which is given below.

$$PL(i) = \beta \left[\frac{6}{24} F(i) + \frac{15}{24} F(i + 1) + \frac{3}{24} F(i + 2) \right] [pers\text{-}h] \qquad (4.5)$$

There are different ways to compute β depending on the availability of data. With the MotionTech case, it is possible to compute it by using the ratio of direct labour cost over the sales price, η. The amount of direct labour per product, β, can then be computed according to the following formula:

$$\beta = \eta \frac{PR_s}{HR_m} \tag{4.6}$$

where PR_s is the sales price in *c.u.* and HR_m is the hourly rate of direct labour in *c.u./h*.

To obtain the number of required workers, $PL(i)$ must be divided by the number of working hours per month, $WH_m = 136\,h$ (4 weeks at $36\,h/week$). Thus we obtain finally:

$$P_w(i) = \eta \frac{PR_s}{HR_m \times WH_m} \left[\frac{6}{24}F(i) + \frac{15}{24}F(i+1) + \frac{3}{24}F(i+2) \right] \tag{4.7}$$

Table 4.3   Required number of direct workers according to the production load for forecasted demand.

Month	1	2	3	4	5	6	7	8	9
12N	28	28	30	31	33	34	34	29	8
16N	32	33	35	37	38	40	40	34	9
24N	19	20	21	22	24	25	25	21	6
35N	16	16	17	17	18	19	19	16	5
Total	95	97	103	107	143	118	118	100	28

The result of applying Eq. (4.7) to the MotionTech forecast is given in Table 4.3. For instance, the computation for the month 5 of product 16N is explained below:

$$P_w(5)16N = 0.087 \frac{650}{43 \times 136} \left[\frac{6}{24}3800 + \frac{15}{24}3900 + \frac{3}{24}4150 \right] = 38$$

The projected number of required direct workers, the production load, must now be compared with the projected available capacity, i.e. the number of available workers. For that purpose, additional data are required to know the company's projected capacity in term of the number of available direct workers, which is shown in Table 4.4.

We can observe that the number of available direct workers does not correspond to the required one. In other words, production load and production capacity are imbalanced. In such a situation, it is difficult to pursue

Table 4.4   Projected number of available workers in production.

Month	1	2	3	4	5	6	7	8	9
Total	143	143	139	131	124	121	127	127	140

the demand following strategy. We must therefore adjust the plan so that it will not exceed the available capacity (assuming that the total capacity will remain stable during the upcoming months).

4.2.4   *Balancing available workers capacity and required workers*

The following list summarises how MotionTech is developing its production plan while pursuing a mixed strategy as a main stream.

(a) The company's production should always meet the forecasted sales; this means that the projected available balance (the inventory) of the finished product at the end of each planning period must always be ≥ 0.
(b) The balance of available direct workers (by computing the difference, $load - capacity$) must always be $\cong 0$.
(c) The company wants to assure the stock of finished products at the end of the planning horizon (month 9) that corresponds approximately to coverage of 0.5 period (i.e. the average demand of 2 weeks).

Since it is not easy to meet all such conditions, an iterative trial-and-error process is required until that the company finds an acceptable solution. Table 4.5 illustrates one of the feasible solutions.

Table 4.5   Feasible aggregate plan for MotionTech.

Month	1	2	3	4	5	6	7	8	9
12N	4760	4845	4930	3965	2925	2010	1420	1775	3685
16N	5695	5610	5780	4680	3420	2340	1660	2075	4290
24N	3230	3060	3315	1935	1350	940	2350	1200	2475
35N	2380	2550	2465	1440	1020	700	1750	900	1870
Total	16065	16065	16490	13260	9720	6720	4720	5950	12320

Table 4.5 illustrates that, foreseeing a sharp decrease in capacity during the months from 5 to 8, anticipated production should be planned to make enough products during the months 1 to 4.

Table 4.6   Projected available balance according to the established AP.

Month	1	2	3	4	5	6	7	8	9
12N	1960	3955	5985	6900	6575	5235	3105	1330	1665
16N	2345	4655	7035	8115	7735	6175	3685	1610	2000
24N	1330	2590	3955	4555	4340	3440	2030	830	1055
35N	990	2030	3045	3510	3350	2670	1620	720	890
Total	6615	13230	20020	23080	22000	17520	10440	4490	5610

Table 4.7   Projected production load: required number of direct workers according to the established AP.

Month	1	2	3	4	5	6	7	8	9
12N	58	57	49	37	26	19	23	233	19
16N	40	41	43	45	47	49	49	41	14
24N	24	25	26	28	29	30	31	26	9
35N	20	20	20	21	22	23	24	20	7
Total	142	143	138	131	124	121	127	120	48

Table 4.8   Projected capacity, number of required workers, and balance.

Month	1	2	3	4	5	6	7	8	9
Available	143	143	139	131	124	121	127	127	140
Required	142	143	138	131	124	121	127	120	48
Balance	1	0	1	0	0	0	0	7	92

Another point to be noted is that the production load of the last two periods of the planning horizon (months 8 and 9) is incomplete since the load of those period is under the influence of forecasted sales for the periods 10 and 11, which are still not known.

Computing the projected available balance

Let us consider the computation of the projected available balance (i.e. projected stock level), $SP(i)$, in month i. It is obtained by the following relation:

$$SP(i) = SP(i-1) + AP(i) - F(i) \qquad (4.8)$$

where $SP(i)$ is the projected available balance at the end of period i, $AP(i)$ is the anticipated volume of finished products entering into the inventory in month i, and $F(i)$ is the forecasted sales amount in month i. In general, $SP(0)$ means the on-hand inventory of finished products. A high level of projected available balance entails a high inventory carrying cost. The inventory carrying cost will be presented in detail in Chapter 5.

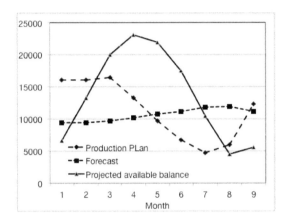

Fig. 4.14   Evolution of forecasted sales, aggregate plan, and projected available balance.

As for the computation method, for month 5 and product 16N, Eq. (4.8) gives the following result:

$$SP(5)_{16N} = 8115 + 3420 - 3800 = 7735$$

In Fig. 4.14 the comparison of three computed values is plotted. As we can see, the anticipated production leads to the following consequences:

(1) In the AP, the amount of finished product requirement is higher than the forecasted amount during the months from 1 to 4;
(2) On the contrary, during the months from 5 to 8, the amount of required finished products in the AP is lower than the forecasted amount;
(3) The projected available balance (inventory) increases during the months from 1 to 4;
(4) The projected available balance (inventory) decreases during the months from 5 to 8.

Computing the projected cash out for the payment to suppliers

According to Fig. 4.6, in order to assure product sales in week j, there are components required for the production step 2 which should be delivered from the suppliers in week $(j-5)$. The payment term is 4 weeks after the delivery, which means in week $(j-5)+4 = j-1$, as illustrated in Fig. 4.15.

Month i	1			2			3				
Monthly forecast F(i)	F(1)			F(2)			F(3)				
Week j	1	2	3	4	5	6	7	8	9	10	11	12
Sales forecast (weekly)								F				
Production Step		S1	S1	S2	S2	S3	S3					
Supply Leadtime	SI	SI	SI									
Payment term				W1	W2	W3	Pay					

Fig. 4.15   Purchasing material for the production step 2 for the delivery of week 8.

This entails, in week 1, 2, 3, and 4, suppliers must be paid for the components required in the production step 2 and for the amount to be sold in week 2, 3, 4 and 5 respectively, which is shown in Fig. 4.16.

Month i	1			2			3				
Monthly forecast F(i)												
Week j	1	2	3	4	5	6	7	8	9	10	11	12
Sales forecast (weekly)								F				
Production Step		S1	S1	S2	S2	S3	S3					
Supply Leadtime	SI	SI	SI									
Payment term				W1	W2	W3	Pay					
Purchase ratio P(i) & P(i+1)					0.75 F(2)				0.25 F(3)			
P(i) = α(0.75F(i) + 0.25F(i+1))												

Fig. 4.16   Purchasing materials generalised for the second month.

This principle can be generalised to formulate the payment amount in each month. The amount to be sold in each of the weeks 2 to 4 represents $\frac{3}{4}$ of the forecast for month i (4 weeks per month). Similarly, the volume to be sold in week 5 represents $\frac{1}{4}$ of forecast for month $i+1$. Thus, during month i, suppliers must be paid for the components required in production step 2 for $\frac{3}{4}$ of the forecasted amount of month i and $\frac{1}{4}$ of the forecasted amount of month $i+1$. The ratio computation is obtained by combining these distributions:

$$P_{comp}(i)(\text{step 2}) = \alpha(\text{comp})PR_s \left[\frac{3}{4}PR(i) + \frac{1}{4}PR(i+1) \right] [c.u.] \quad (4.9)$$

where α is the ratio of (material cost)/(sales price) and PR_s the sales price (see Table 4.2) A similar approach is applied to computing the purchasing cost for materials required in production step 1. In this case, in week 1,2, 3 and 4 suppliers must be paid for the material required in the production step 1 and for the amount to be sold in week 4, 5, 6 and 7 respectively. The ratio computation becomes then:

$$P_{mat}(i)(\text{step 1}) = \alpha(\text{mat})PR_s \left[\frac{1}{4}PR(i) + \frac{3}{4}PR(i+1)\right] [c.u.] \qquad (4.10)$$

Assume that the material cost is split into two categories: 20% for material costs and 80% for component cost. The two previous equations can be combined as below:

$$P_{total}(i) = \alpha PR_s \left\{ 0.2 \left[\frac{1}{4}PR(i) + \frac{3}{4}PR(i+1)\right] \right.$$

$$\left. + 0.8 \left[\frac{3}{4}PR(i) + \frac{1}{4}PR(i+1)\right] \right\} (c.u.) \qquad (4.11)$$

The application of this equation to the MotionTech AP gives the results presented in Table 4.9. As illustrated, due to the high volume of finished products planned to be available in the period of months 1 to 4, the required cash for payment to the suppliers is also important during the first four months, which is relatively low in months 6 to 8 (Fig. 4.17).

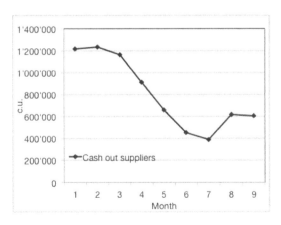

Fig. 4.17   Graphical representation of cash-out to suppliers according to the final AP.

If MotionTech can afford such financial requirement even during the peak payment periods, the current aggregate plan can be accepted as a feasible AP. In next section, we continue developing the lower level planning, i.e. establishing the Master Production Schedule.

Table 4.9   Cash out to suppliers according to the AP and ratio computation (Eq. (4.11)).

Month	1	2	3	4	5	6	7	8	9
12N	287'385	292'485	275'535	216'060	156'285	108'210	92'655	146'610	143'715
16N	368'241	368'518	350'675	275'535	197'730	136'630	117'341	185'266	181'253
24N	269'493	267'686	260'504	201'216	147'071	102'553	87'635	139'931	136'744
35N	292'740	302'430	276'900	217'650	155'160	108'960	92'400	148'740	145'860
Total	1'217'859	1'231'119	1'163'614	910'461	656'246	456'353	390'031	620'548	607'571

Computation of monthly ratios

Frame 1: Production sequences

	Month	i-1				i				i+1				i+2			
	Week	1	2	3	4	5	6	7	8	9	10	11	12	13	14	15	16
Sales forecast													F				
Production steps 1 to 3						M1	M1	M2	M2	M3	M3						
Supply; production step 2						S	S	S									
Payment suppliers components step 2									1	2	3	P					
Supply; production step 1				S	S	S											
Payment suppliers components step 1						1	2	3	P								

Frame 2: Computation of ratios for production load

	i-1				i				i+1				i+2
Load on production month i													
production forecasted amount week 2					2	F							
production forecasted amount week 3					3	3	F						
production forecasted amount week 4					4	4	4	F					
production forecasted amount week 5					5	5	5	5	F				
production forecasted amount week 6					6	6	6	6	6	F			
production forecasted amount week 7					7	7	7	7	7	F			
production forecasted amount week 8					8	8	8	8	8	8	F		
production forecasted amount week 9						9	9	9	9	9	9	F	
production forecasted amount week 10							10	10	10	10	10	10	F
PL(i)=β(6/24F(i) + 15/24F(i+1) + 3/24F(i+2))					6/24				15/24				3/24

Frame 3: Computation of ratios for cash out supplier for components production step 2

	i-1	i				i+1	i+2
Planning cash out suppliers month i							
payment component step 2, forecasted amount week		2	3	4	5		
A(i)=α(3/4F(i) + 1/4F(i+1))		3/4				1/4	0

Frame 4: Computation of ratios for cash out supplier for components production step 1

	i-1	i				i+1	i+2
Planning cash out suppliers month i							
payment component step 1, forecasted amount week		4	5	6	7		
A(i)=α(3/4F(i) + 1/4F(i+1))		1/4				3/4	0

Fig. 4.18 Computation of the monthly ratios for MotionTech — full illustration in Excel.

Figure 4.18 shows an Excel-based way of representing the production load, including the payment terms for suppliers.

4.3 Master production schedule (MPS)

The MPS serves as an operational tool for production management. The elaboration of MPS requires a tight collaboration among different department in a company such as Operations, Sales & Marketing, and Finance departments in order to agree on an approved plan.

Particularly considering manufacturing operations, the purpose of MPS is to know the requirements of all the items of the BoM below level 0. The horizon of the MPS should be of the order of 1.5 to 2 times the cumulative lead-time, i.e. the longest anticipation required (for the procurement of the maximum lead-time of components).

The choice of the planning period (hour, day, week, month) depends on the characteristics and dynamics of each company. In a company delivering heavy and expensive equipment that needs a year between order and delivery, a monthly period may be adequate. On the contrary, in a company producing consumer goods, a daily planning period can be applied.

The MPS should be revised regularly while following new incoming orders and taking into account of changes in the production and inventory status (this is often done daily or weekly, or even continuously). A complete revision with new forecasts is generally done at a lower frequency, since it requires an expensive and sophisticated procedure (this is often done on a monthly basis).

4.3.1   *Input to the MPS*

The development of the MPS is based upon the AP and other additional elements, as illustrated in Fig. 4.19:

- The update of forecasted demand with the integration of confirmed orders, i.e. the values coming from the company's customer order book.
- The inventory (on-hand inventory) and production status (i.e. already ordered production) must be taken into account as initial conditions for the planning.
- The available production capacity puts also constraints on the planning process.

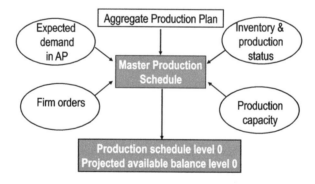

Fig. 4.19   Schematic representation of the MPS development procedure.

The MPS considers, in general, finished products (individual real product). However if the number of product variants is too high to deal with all the individual products, it is also possible to use fictive finished products representing a historically known composition of variants. Such a structure is called as super BoM.

4.3.2 Output from the MPS

The output of the MPS is a production schedule of these finished products (level 0), as well as the projected available balance of these products at the end of each planning period. Let us take a look at the main characteristics and useful conventions for the MPS generation:

- Time phasing: planning and calculation procedure based on time buckets, the planning periods.
- All planned production orders PO_t and launched production orders LO_t for a given planning period t are considered to be available at the beginning of planning period t.
- The planned demand PP_t (disaggregated AP values) is offset by the firm customer orders CO_t (they don't add since the customer orders which have taken place (i.e. confirmed as a firm order) were already considered in forecasting as potential demands).
- The projected available balance SP_t is the quantity available at the end of period t.

Let t_1 be the first period of the MPS, i.e. the period immediately following the present time which is t_0. The calculation procedure starts with the current status given below:

- On-hand inventory: Inventory SP_0 at the end of period 0;
- Launched orders LO_t: Production orders currently in execution (they have been launched in the past) and with planned delivery in any future period t.

Under these initial conditions, the main planning procedure can start. It needs, for the whole planning horizon H (h planning periods), the planned demand PP_t (obtained by the disaggregation of the AP monthly value) and the customer firm orders CO_t (contained in the order book) for all the finished products.

The MPS generation requires the disaggregation and time phasing. As the AP is developed at an aggregate level (for example, product family), the values of expected production volume must be disaggregated into each product of that family. In addition, the planning period used in the

Aggregate Production is generally larger than that of the MPS; consequently a further disaggregation of the time scale is necessary.

Now let us assume the following situation, which is illustrated in Table 4.10:

- $PP_t(p)$: the expected demand in a disaggregated production plan for a single product p at period t;
- The on hand inventory $SP_0 = 30$;
- One production order $LO_2 = 30$ (due date in period 2) has been launched in a former period;
- The lot size for final assembly of the finished product must be a multiple of 30.

Table 4.10   Initial situation before generating a new MPS.

period t	1	2	3	4	5	6	7	8	9	10
$PP_t(p)$	10	10	10	10	15	20	30	20	20	10
Firm customer order CO_t	20	2		35		10				
Launched Order LO_t		30								
On-hand inventory $SP_0 = 30$										

The MPS generation proceeds period by period, starting at period $t = 1$ and ending at period $t = h$, for the purpose of creating relevant production order, PO_t, according to the following formulas:

$$PO_t = \Lambda\{max[PP_t(p), CO_t] + Ss - SP_{t-1} - LO_t\} \qquad (4.12)$$

$$SP_t = SP_{t-1} + (PO_t + LO_t) - max[PP_t(p), CO_t] \qquad (4.13)$$

where Λ is a function describing the lot sizing policy, and Ss is the safety stock.

In this example, the function Λ is:

$$\Lambda = 30n, n \in N \qquad (4.14)$$

with $30(n-1) < \{max[PP_t(p), CO_t] + Ss - SP_{t-1} - LO_t\} < 30n$.

The result of this procedure is illustrated in Table 4.11 for the previous case and considering the safety stock policy, $Ss = 10$. The MPS result shows the delivery plan corresponding to the series of planned orders, PO_t: one lot of 30 in periods 4, 5, 7 and 9.

The planning procedure should work on minimising the projected available balance at the end of each planning period. In the above-presented

Table 4.11   Situation after the generation of the MPS.

period t	1	2	3	4	5	6	7	8	9	10
$PP_t(p)$	10	10	10	10	15	20	30	20	20	10
Firm customer order CO_t	20	2		35		10				
Launched Order LO_t		30								
Planned Order PO_t				30	30		30	30	30	
Projected available bal. SP_t On-hand inventory $SP_0 = 30$	10	30	20	15	30	10	10	20	30	20

example, the possible minimum value of SP shall be 10 in an ideal case with the safety stock level $Ss = 10$. However, due to the lot-sizing policy (multiple of 30), the projected available balance is generally larger than the safety stock. The established MPS provides a general plan for satisfying the expected market requirements. The next step consists of validating the available resource capacity so as to confirm this plan as a feasible solution. Before presenting the resource capacity validation in Section Capacity Planning, we will apply the method of MPS to the MotionTech case study in the next subsection.

4.3.3   *Application of the MPS to MotionTech*

In the MotionTech example, we will take the 16N product family as example. A similar process would have to be applied to the other three product families. Let us assume that the 16N family contains only two types of finished products (level 0), 16N-A and 16N-B. As mentioned previously, the MPS preparation requires the disaggregation of aggregate product family as well as the disaggregation of time bucket, i.e. the size of period such as from monthly to weekly period. To disaggregate the demand data on the AP level, we have to know the expected product mix of the 16N family. In a company, such information may be obtained from the sales history (i.e. direct intrinsic data), or with the help of sales and marketing department (i.e. expert judgement). In the MotionTech case, let us assume that the following product mix is used:

- 45% 16N-A
- 55% 16N-B

In the context of this case study, a stable product mix is assumed. However this may change with time in a real sales environment, which can happen particularly when products are in different stages of their lifetime, one being introduced while the other becoming obsolete. In such a case, a time-dependent product mix shall be used which will not be dealt with in our case study.

As a reminder, the computation of the MPS requires the following data:

- Expected demand coming from the Aggregate Production Plan;
- Firm customer orders from the Order book;
- On-hand inventory of each finished product;
- Safety stock requirement of each finished product;
- Lot-size of the final assembly shop;
- Launched orders in the final assembly shop.

Frame 1: Production Plan

Month	1	2	3	4	5	6
16N	5695	5610	5780	4680	3420	2340
16N-A	2563	2525	2601	2106	1539	1053
16N-B	3132	3086	3179	2574	1881	1287

Frame 2: Order Book

Month	1				2				3				4				5				6			
Week	1	2	3	4	5	6	7	8	9	10	11	12	13	14	15	16	17	18	19	20	21	22	23	24
16N-A	385	402	375	378	223	152	145	123	75	65	48	41	24	0	0	12								
16N-B	475	457	449	467	398	363	340	329	155	124	105	107	78	34	0	43								

Frame 3: On-hand inventory & safety stock

	On-hand	Safety stock
16N-A	850	800
16N-B	1035	1000

Frame 4: Lot-sizing policy

	Final assembly		
16N-A	min.	40	multiple of 20
16N-B	min.	40	multiple of 20

Frame 5: Launched orders, final assembly

Week	1	2	3	4	5
16N-A	620	660			
16N-B	800	800			

Fig. 4.20   Data for the MotionTech 16N product family.

Figure 4.20 provides these data for the 16N product family of Motion-Tech. For the sake of simplicity, only the first six months of the planning horizon are presented with the following information.

- Frame 1: Initial Aggregate Production Plan with product level disaggregation.
- Frame 2: Customer order book.
- Frame 3: On-hand inventory and safety stock requirement for both products.
- Frame 4: Lot size in the final assembly process for both products.
- Frame 5: Launched orders in the final assembly shop of each product.

The second type of disaggregation deals with the time phasing, i.e. disaggregating the monthly volume into the MPS periodic volume. In our case, this process concerns the distribution of the monthly amount of AP_i into the weekly amount while creating PP_j values for week j. The next step concerns the computation of gross requirement based on the firm customer orders which have been confirmed in the company's Order Book. The initial situation for starting the MPS is illustrated in Table 4.12.

The gross requirement of the MPS does not take the current situation of the company into account, such as the on-hand inventory or the launched orders. To compute the net requirement, we must take such information into consideration. By applying Eq. (4.12) and Eq. (4.13) to the MotionTech 16N products, the results concerning the first three months are obtained as illustrated in Tables 4.13 and 4.14.

Let us consider product 16N-A in week 10 to describe the computation details.

- The gross requirement, GR_t, is obtained by computing $max[PP_t, CO_t] = max[650, 65] = 650$.
- The required safety stock for product 16N-A is $Ss = 800$.
- The projected available balance of the previous period $(t = 9)$ is $SP_9 = 812$.
- There are no launched orders for period 10. Therefore $LO_{10} = 0$.

Thus the net requirement of the product in period 10, NR_{10} is computed as below:

$$NR_{10} = 650 + 800 - 812 - 0 = 638$$

By applying the lot-size (min. 40, multiple of 20) to the net requirement of 638, the final amount of planned order receipt results in $PO_{10} = 640$.

Computing the projected actual inventory of finished products

Now, based on the computation results of planned production order and the forecasted actual demand, we can verify the actual projected inventory status for the purpose of knowing the evolution of the buffer stock. Table 4.15 shows the first three month actual inventory of 16N-A. When we compute the net requirement and the planned order receipt in the MPS, we have considered the gross requirement derived from the AP. As the AP was created pursuing a mixed strategy, the product level actual inventory during the sales and operations will evolve differently than the projected available balance used during the MPS planning procedure.

Table 4.12 Gross requirement for generating the MPS of the MotionTech 16N products.

Month	1				2				3			
Week	1	2	3	4	5	6	7	8	9	10	11	12
16N-A	641	641	641	641	631	631	631	631	650	650	650	650
16N-B	783	783	773	783	772	772	772	772	795	795	795	795
Total	1424	1424	1424	1424	1403	1403	1403	1403	1445	1445	1445	1445

Table 4.13   Final assembly schedule for 16N-A finished products.

Month	1				2				3			
Week	1	2	3	4	5	6	7	8	9	10	11	12
Gross req.	641	641	641	641	631	631	631	631	650	650	650	650
Proj. stock	829	848	807	806	815	804	813	802	812	802	812	802
LO	620	660										
PO receit			600	640	640	620	640	620	660	640	660	640
PO release	600	640	640	620	640	620	660	640	660	640	540	520

The projected actual inventory of finished products can also be computed according to the following formula:

$$SP_t(Prod) = SP_{t-1}(Prod) + PO_t + LO_t - GR_t$$

where $SP_t(Prod)$ is the actual finished product inventory at the end of period t. However, in this case, the gross requirement, GR_t, should indicate the independent demand obtained from the disaggregated forecast, or the firm customer orders (if it is higher than the forecasted amount) of the considered finished product for period t.

For product 16N-A in period 10, this gives:

$$SP_{10}(\text{16N-A}) = 3175 + 640 - 383 = 3432$$

The full results are given in Fig. 4.21. As can be seen in Fig. 4.21, the actual inventory of finished product 16N-A varies considerably over the planning horizon. This is due to the fact that the production feeds the inventory according to the AP (the modified demand), whereas the inventory deliveries take place according to the market demand from customers; i.e. either based on forecast or firm customer orders. Such a result is plausible since anticipated production has been introduced in the AP.

4.4   Capacity planning

Like many concepts in operations management, capacity management may concern several issues of different nature. The following example shows typical questions related to the capacity management:

- Aroma production company *Profood*: Will the total production capacity of the 15 world factories be sufficient to cover our market needs in the next five years?

Fig. 4.21   Evolution of the actual finished product inventory.

- Printing machine company *Fawig*: How many workers should be present tomorrow in the assembly shop?
- Medical device SME *Medtech*: Should the management team plan to hire new people for the next quarter, or prepare itself for short-term, limited unemployment?
- Electrical motor manufacturer *EMC*: How should next years' production volume is distributed between our manufacturing units in Sweden and Switzerland?
- Electrical component distribution company *Distrilec*: What transportation capacity should we plan for next week?

As the above-mentioned examples illustrate, capacity management can take different forms. It can cover from long-term strategic issues to short-term operational decisions. It can also relate the square meters of a factory floor, cubic meters of storage space, weekly production volume, or daily person-hours. However, these all have one thing in common: the need to find an optimal equilibrium between the required and the available resources. This means a balanced solution between performance and cost, e.g. the lead-time and person-hours cost. In the context of this book, we will focus on medium and short-term capacity management, without dealing too much with long-term strategic capacity management.

4.4.1   Basic concepts and definitions

Production load and production capacity are terms that are often used interchangeably. The two terms, however, have different meanings.

Table 4.14 Final assembly schedule for 16N-B finished products.

Month	1				2				3			
Week	1	2	3	4	5	6	7	8	9	10	11	12
Gross req.	783	783	783	783	772	772	772	772	795	795	795	795
Proj. stock	1052	1069	1006	1003	1011	1019	1007	1015	1000	1005	1010	1015
LO	800	800										
PO receipt			720		780	780	760	780	780	800	800	800
PO release	720	780	780	780	760	780	780	800	800	800	640	640

Table 4.15 Computation of actual inventory for 16N-A.

Month	1				2				3			
Week	1	2	3	4	5	6	7	8	9	10	11	12
Forecasted req.	377	377	377	377	371	371	371	371	383	383	383	383
LO and PO	620	660	600	640	640	620	640	620	660	640	660	640
Actual proj. inv.	1093	1376	1599	1862	2131	2380	2649	2898	3175	3432	3709	3966

Production capacity is the maximum amount of work that can be processed in a production unit (work centre, department, and factory) within a given planning period.

Production load is the amount of work to be processed by a production unit in a specific planning period. The production load on a production unit is the sum of the required hours for all the planned and launched orders to be executed by the unit in a specified planning period.

To summarise, the production capacity is used to describe the available resources whereas the production load indicates the required resources. Finding an optimal equilibrium between the required and the available resources cannot be achieved by a straightforward process. Rather than applying complex algorithm, it is still common in companies to find a simple way of capacity adjustment. Assuming that the dominant hypothesis of production is deterministic with stable material flow, the following simple assessments may take place:

- Production is feasible if available production capacity is at least equal to the expected production load.
- Production is not feasible if available production capacity is lower than the expected production load.

This simplistic view tends to load the production system as close as possible to its available capacity. At first glance, it seems to be a solution to reaching a low level of direct costs. However in practice, if company operates according to such a principle, it is inevitable to reach a high level of work in process (WIP), long lead-times and poor responsiveness with poor logistic performances, which entails low customer satisfaction as well as high inventory costs.

A more sophisticated but realistic method tries to take into account the stochastic nature of production considering that:

- Production is always feasible if available capacity is larger than zero.
- Lead-time and WIP levels grow continuously with the increase of utilisation rate (ratio of used to available resources).
- Responsiveness decreases continuously with the increase of utilisation rate.

This view tends to adjust the utilisation rate (i.e. the available capacity) according to predefined performance objectives, such as maximum lead-time and/or minimum responsiveness. It may lead to the utilisation

Table 4.16   Deterministic versus stochastic approaches of capacity management.

	Deterministic view (traditional)	Stochastic view (more realistic)
Basic assumptions	Based on deterministic demand and regular material flow.	Based on the stochastic nature.
		Lead-time and WIP levels grow continuously with increasing utilisation rate.
Feasibility	If utilisation rate is <100%, then production is feasible. Otherwise it is not feasible.	Production is always feasible. Lead-time increases with increasing utilisation rate.
Approaches to production line design	Adjusting available capacity as close as possible to the expected production load (utilisation rate close to 100%).	Adjusting available capacity according to predefined performance objectives (upper limit for lead-times, lower limit for responsiveness).
	Leads to high WIP, long lead-times, poor responsiveness.	Leads to lower utilisation rate low WIP, short lead-times, good responsiveness.

rates far below 100%, which are less attractive from the point of view of a manager if this person does not have a good understanding of the stochastic aspects of production. Table 4.16 summarises both visions and underlines their main characteristics.

4.4.2   *Hierarchical approach to capacity and production planning*

If the production planning follows a hierarchical approach, the capacity planning should be achieved in parallel with the level-by-level planning so as to verify the load and capacity balancing at different levels. The hierarchical capacity planning uses gross requirements as input, and provides as output the estimation of production load at a given level. This load is then compared with the expected available production capacity. If the load balancing cannot be achieved as expected, either the production plan should be adapted or the available capacity must be adjusted.

Subsequently, a specific methodology of capacity planning is associated with each level of production planning, which is shown on Fig. 4.22.

Aggregate capacity planning and aggregate plan

The purpose of aggregate capacity planning, which is the highest level of capacity planning, is to verify whether the available production capacity

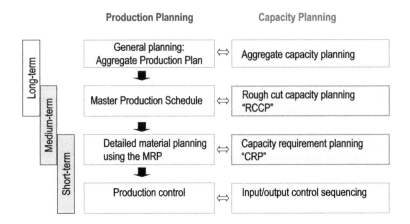

Fig. 4.22   Capacity planning and production planning.

might satisfy the expected production load at the aggregate level. The capacity is measured in an aggregate form, such as the total person-hours per month, the total liquidity (for purchasing) in quarterly financial volume, the total output rate of a factory, or the total inventory volume.

The main characteristics of the aggregate capacity planning are given below.

- It considers the planning horizon of about 6 to 24 months, with periodic (approximately monthly) update;
- It considers the aggregate level of product demand, that is, the demand of a finished product family stated in common terms like volume per month;
- It takes aggregate resources into account, such as the planned available production capacity of a large production unit (e.g. the assembly factory) stated in common terms like person-hours per month;
- It compares the available production capacity with the expected production load derived from the expected aggregate demand;
- According to the result of the comparison, it helps make a decision on modification either of the production plan and/or of the available production capacity.

The general aims of aggregate capacity planning are summarised below:

- Minimise the total cost over the planning horizon;
- Maximise customer service;

- Minimise inventory levels;
- Minimise changes in workforce levels;
- Minimise changes in production rates;
- Maximise utilisation of plant and equipment avoiding under performance and/or overtime.

As a reminder, a mixed strategy consists of partially adapting the production capacity to the production load. This strategy can be supported by an aggregate capacity planning, and is most often chosen since it allows minimisation of the required inventory while restraining the production capacity changes within manageable boundaries. In the creation of the Aggregate Plan for MotionTech, we have used the aggregate capacity planning to find a feasible solution as a compromise between load versus capacity balancing. In the following sections, we discuss the three major methods of aggregate capacity planning.

4.4.3 *Rough cut capacity planning and master production schedule*

Rough Cut Capacity Planning (RCCP) is a group of techniques that provides an early warning of potential problems with available resources. It uses simplified capacity model while concentrating on the analysis of critical or bottleneck resources. The purpose of the RCCP is to provide a first rough validation of the feasibility of the MPS in terms of resource availability. There are three main RCCP techniques, described below in increasing order of complexity and accuracy:

- Capacity Planning using Overall Factors (CPOF), based on primitive production data without looking for detailed product information;
- Bill of Capacity (BoC), based on more specific information about product resource requirements;
- Resource Profile (RP), based on the detailed description of product resource requirements taking into account the production lead-times.

The common characteristics of RCCP are described below.

- It considers the gross requirement of MPS items (level 0 of the BoM);
- It allows the rough estimation of the global production load;
- It allows the rough estimation of the purchase volume;
- It helps check the availability of production capacity of critical production units;
- It works without computing net requirement computation.

4.4.4   *Capacity planning using overall factors (CPOF)*

This method is based on overall load factors derived from standard or historical data of finished products. The method is simple enough to be computed manually without a particular support of computers.

The CPOF requires the following input data:

- Gross requirement of the MPS per finished product
- Overall load factors: historical load distribution per production centre to be planned
- Cost structure per finished product

The CPOF generates the following output:

- Overall production load in terms of labour
- Overall production load for machines and other equipment
- Purchasing volume

The procedure of the CPOF is illustrated below:

(1) Identify the production centres i to analyse.
(2) Determine the production load distribution α_i of the centres i to be planned on the basis of historical data.
(3) Compute the global production load per period L_t on the basis of the MPS gross requirement per period t, GR_t and of the global work volume w_k per finished product k.

$$L_t = \sum_k GR_{t,k} \times w_k \qquad (4.15)$$

(4) Compute the load L_{it} per centre i for each period t on the basis of the global production load L_t and of the historical distribution coefficients α_i.

$$L_{it} = L_t \times \alpha_i \qquad (4.16)$$

Application of the CPOF to MotionTech

Based on the MPS gross requirement of MotionTech presented in Table 4.12, let us apply the CPOF method. For the sake of simplicity, we will consider only the 16N product family and a limited planning horizon of 12 weeks.

For the purpose of validating the rough capacity, the aggregate load on large production sectors might be enough.

Table 4.17   Historical load distribution for the 16N product family.

Production sector	Historical load distribution	Work volume
Assembly	46%	0.6
Manufacturing	24%	0.32
Coil winding	30%	0.4
Total	100%	1.32

In the MotionTech case, the following three production sectors will be taken into account, and the collected data are illustrated in Table 4.17:

- Assembly: motor assembly, stator assembly and rotor assembly
- Manufacturing: collector cup manufacturing and shaft machining
- Coil winding manufacturing

We can now compute the global production load per period applying Eq. (4.15). The global work volume per product is given as $w_k = 1.32\,(pers\text{-}h)$. In a real situation, it can be computed, for example, on the basis of the sales price, the direct labour cost ratio and the hourly rate. The results are given in Frame 1 of Fig. 4.23. For example, the global load for period 10 is obtained as follows:

$$L_{10} = (650 + 795) \times 1.32 = 1909$$

The next step consists of distributing this global production load among the three production sectors according to the coefficients α defined in Table 4.17 and by applying Eq. (4.16). The results are provided in Frame 2 of Fig. 4.23. The following lines of computation explain how the value of period 10 are obtained:

$$L_{assembly,\,10} = 1909 \times 0.46 = 878\,h$$

$$L_{manufacturing,\,10} = 1909 \times 0.24 = 458\,h$$

$$L_{coil\ winding,\,10} = 1909 \times 0.30 = 573\,h$$

The purchase volume can be obtained in the same way but considering the material cost instead of the direct production cost. Assuming that a material cost, c_k, which is the total cost of purchased material per product equals $65\,c.u.$ the results are presented in Frame 3 of Fig. 4.23. For period 10, the result is obtained as explained below:

$$PV_{10} = \sum_k GR_{10,k} \times c_k = 1445 \times 65 = 93925\,c.u.$$

Frame 1: Global load computation (h)

Week	1	2	3	4	5	6	7	8	9	10	11	12
16N	1881	1881	1881	1881	1853	1853	1853	1853	1909	1909	1909	1909

Frame 2: Load on production sectors (h)

Week	1	2	3	4	5	6	7	8	9	10	11	12
Assembly	865	865	865	865	853	853	853	853	878	878	878	878
Manufacturing	451	451	451	451	445	445	445	445	458	458	458	458
Coil winding	564	564	564	564	556	556	556	556	573	573	573	573

Frame 3: Purchase volume (c.u.)

Week	1	2	3	4	5	6	7	8	9	10	11	12
	92560	92560	92560	92560	91195	91195	91195	91195	93925	93925	93925	93925

Fig. 4.23   CPOF computation results for the 16N product family.

4.4.5   *Bill of Capacity (BoC)*

This method helps establish a direct link between individual finished products in the MPS and the production load on individual production centres. To do this, the required resources to produce one unit of finished product should be split into all production centres which work on its production. This two dimensional relation between finished products and production centres is called Bill of Capacity (BoC). Table 4.18 shows an example of the BoC data for two products 16N-A and 16N-B.

Table 4.18   Bill of Capacity for product A and product B.

	A	B
Production centre	Total time/unit $[h/pcs.]$	Total time/unit $[h/pcs.]$
100	0.05	1.30
200	0.70	0.55
300	0.50	0.00
Total time/unit	1.25	1.85

The BoC method requires more data at the level of finished products, which makes its application more complex than the CPOF method. Without the support of a computer, it is difficult to apply the BoC method to each product and centre. The following elements are required input and expected output of BoC:

Input data for the Bill of Capacity

- MPS gross requirement per finished product
- BoC data table: specific production load per finished product for each production centre labour
- Cost structure per finished product

Output from the BoC method

- Production load in terms of labour for each production centre
- Production load for machines and other equipment for each production centre
- Purchasing volume

The computation procedure of the BoC method is given below:

(1) Identify the production centres i to be analysed.
(2) Compute the load L_{itk} per period t and per centre i on the basis of the MPS gross requirement and of the BoC $w_{i,k}$ of each centre i to be planned for each finished product k.

$$L_{itk} = \sum_k GR_{t,k} \times w_{i,k} \qquad (4.17)$$

(3) Compute the total load L_{it} for each centre i to be planned by adding the specific loads L_{itk} of each finished product k.

$$L_{it} = \sum_k L_{itk} = \sum_k GR_{t,k} \times w_{i,k} \qquad (4.18)$$

Application of the BoC to MotionTech

In this subsection, we apply the BoC method to the MotionTech 16N product family, product A and B, based on the same MPS gross requirement already presented in Table 4.12. The difference between CPOF and BoC is the level of detail concerning the production load data that both methods require. With the BoC model, we need the single production load of each product on the concerned production centres. In this case study, we assume that the two finished products, 16N-A and 16N-B, are manufacture through almost identical production operations. Resultantly, there is no difference in the values of their respective BoC, as can be seen in Fig. 4.24. However, it is not a general rule to apply to other manufacturing cases. It is possible that different finished products belonging to the same product family can have different BoC data specific to each of them.

Operation	Production center	Production load [h/pcs.]	
		16N-A	16N-B
Motor assembly	100 - assembly shop A	0.1	0.1
Stator assembly	200 –asssembly shop B	0.3	0.3
Collector cup manufacturing	300 – injection molding	0.02	0.02
Rotor assembly	100 – assembly shop A	0.2	0.2
Shaft machining	400 – machine shop	0.3	0.3
Coil winding	500 –coil winding shop	0.4	0.4
Total production load	100, 200, 300, 400, 500	1.32	1.32

Fig. 4.24   Bill of Capacity for products 16N-A and 16N-B.

We now compute the production load per period for each production centre applying the equation Eq. (4.17) using the MPS gross requirement given in Table 4.12. The total load on each production centre is then obtained by adding the contribution of each product according to the equation Eq. (4.18). Figure 4.25 provides the final results of the BoC method.

For the purpose of illustrating the detailed computation, let us take period 10 and production centre 500 as example, which is given below.

$$L_{500,10} = \sum_k L_{500,10,k} = \sum_k GR_{10,k} \times w_{500,k}$$

$$= GR_{10,16N-A} \times GR_{10,16N-B} \times w_{500,16N-B}$$

$$L_{500,10} = 650 \times 0.4 + 795 \times 0.4 = 578\,h$$

4.4.6   *Resource profiles*

This method is also based on the volume of the required resources, distributed over each production centre, for producing one unit of a given

Product 16N-A												
Week	1	2	3	4	5	6	7	8	9	10	11	12
100 - assembly shop	192	192	192	192	189	189	189	189	195	195	195	195
200 –asssembly shop	192	192	192	192	189	189	189	189	195	195	195	195
300 – injection molding	13	13	13	13	13	13	13	13	13	13	13	13
400 – machine shop	192	192	192	192	189	189	189	189	195	195	195	195
500 –coil winding shop	256	256	256	256	252	252	252	252	260	260	260	260
Product 16N-B												
Week	1	2	3	4	5	6	7	8	9	10	11	12
100 - assembly shop	235	235	235	235	232	232	232	232	239	239	239	239
200 –asssembly shop	235	235	235	235	232	232	232	232	239	239	239	239
300 – injection molding	16	16	16	16	15	15	15	15	16	16	16	16
400 – machine shop	235	235	235	235	232	232	232	232	239	239	239	239
500 –coil winding shop	313	313	313	313	309	309	309	309	318	318	318	318
Total load on production centers												
Week	1	2	3	4	5	6	7	8	9	10	11	12
100 - assembly shop	427	427	427	427	421	421	421	421	434	434	434	434
200 –asssembly shop	427	427	427	427	421	421	421	421	434	434	434	434
300 – injection molding	28	28	28	28	28	28	28	28	29	29	29	29
400 – machine shop	427	427	427	427	421	421	421	421	434	434	434	434
500 –coil winding shop	570	570	570	570	561	561	561	561	578	578	578	578

Fig. 4.25   BoC computation results for the 16N product family.

finished product. In addition, it takes into account the average lead-times associated with each of the concerned production centres.

Subsequently, the Resource Profiles (RP) method uses the distribution of the required resources for each production centre over corresponding periods of lead-time. This load versus time function is called the Resource Profile. Since the Resource Profile data should be obtained considering each production centre and each finished product, this method requires more data collection and its application is more complex than the BoC. The support of a computer system is therefore necessary. The following set of lists summarises the input and output data of the Resource Profiles method.

Input data for resource profiles

- MPS gross requirement
- Resource Profile: specific load and lead-times per finished product for each production centre to be planned

Output from the resource profiles

- Production load in terms of labour for each production centre
- Production load for machines and other equipment for each production centre

Procedure for resource profiles method

(1) Identify the production centres i to be analysed.
(2) Compute the production load L_{itk} per period t and per production centre i on the basis of the MPS gross requirement $GR_{i,k}$ and of the resource profile $R_{i,k}$ of each finished product k, where p is the lead-time index (p period before the delivery).

$$L_{i,t,k} = \sum_{p=0}^{P} \left(GR_{(t+p),k} \times R_{i,k,p} \right) \tag{4.19}$$

As an example, for production centre i, period 2 and product A, the RP will be computed as below.

$$L_{i,2,A} = GR_{2,A}R_{i,A,0} + GR_{3,A}R_{i,A,1} + GR_{4,A}R_{i,A,2} + \ldots + GR_{2+p,A}R_{i,A,P}$$

(3) Compute the total load $L_{i,t}$ for each production centre i by adding the computed loads $L_{i,t,k}$ specific to each finished product k.

$$L_{i,t} = \sum_{k} L_{itk} = \sum_{k} \sum_{p=0}^{P} \left(GR_{(t+p),k} \times R_{i,k,p} \right) \tag{4.20}$$

Application of the RP method to MotionTech

For the purpose of applying the RP method to the MotionTech 16N product family, we will use the production structure of MotionTech and the BoC data. The average production lead-times of all three production steps is 2 weeks, and the supply lead-time is 3 weeks. The Bill Of Capacity for this micro-motor is defined in Fig. 4.24. The first step is to establish the Resource Profiles data table by distributing the production loads, given in the BoC, over the corresponding lead-time. In the 16N products of MotionTech, let us assume that we are dealing with 5 different production centres, which are given below.

(1) Centre 100 assembly shop A
(2) Centre 200 assembly shop B
(3) Centre 300 injection moulding shop
(4) Centre 400 machine shop
(5) Centre 500 coil winding shop

Product 16N-A												
Week	1	2	3	4	5	6	7	8	9	10	11	12
100 - assembly shop A	191	190	190	189	192	193	194	195	177	170	164	158
200 –asssembly shop B	191	189	189	189	191	195	195	195	183	158	158	158
300 – injection molding	13	13	13	13	13	13	13	13	12	11	11	11
400 – machine shop	189	189	192	195	195	195	177	158	158	158	137	116
500 –coil winding shop	252	252	258	260	260	260	223	211	211	211	168	154
Product 16N-B												
Week	1	2	3	4	5	6	7	8	9	10	11	12
100 - assembly shop A	233	233	232	232	235	236	237	239	216	208	201	193
200 –asssembly shop B	234	232	232	232	234	239	239	239	223	193	193	193
300 – injection molding	16	15	15	15	16	16	16	16	14	13	13	13
400 – machine shop	232	232	235	239	239	239	216	193	193	193	167	141
500 –coil winding shop	309	309	316	318	318	318	273	258	258	258	205	188
Total load on production centers												
Week	1	2	3	4	5	6	7	8	9	10	11	12
100 - assembly shop A	424	423	422	421	427	429	431	434	392	379	365	351
200 –asssembly shop B	425	421	421	421	425	434	434	434	406	351	351	351
300 – injection molding	28	28	28	28	28	29	29	29	26	23	23	23
400 – machine shop	421	421	427	434	434	434	392	351	351	351	304	257
500 –coil winding shop	561	561	574	578	578	578	496	468	468	468	374	342

Fig. 4.26   Production load computed by resource profiles.

Consequently, five resource profiles are provided in Fig. 4.26. The suggested production steps are coherent with the description of the production process presented in the Bill of Operations.

The resource profiles for centres 100 to 500 define the production loads $R_{i,k,p}$ on each centre i per unit of product k, p periods before delivery. Using the known RP data, we can apply the procedure described above to compute the production load.

Now, we can compute the load per period $L_{i,t,k}$ of the products 16N-A and 16N-B by applying Eq. (4.19). Finally, we add the computed loads of each product to find the total load on a specific production centre. The results of these computations are shown in Fig. 4.27.

Some computation examples are provided below for clarity.

$$L_{100,5,16\text{N-A}} = GR_{5,16\text{N-A}} R_{100,16\text{N-A},0} + GR_{6,16\text{N-A}} R_{100,16\text{N-A},1} + \cdots$$
$$+ GR_{9,16\text{N-A}} R_{100,16\text{N-A},4}$$
$$L_{100,5,16\text{N-A}} = 631 \times 0 + 631 \times 0.05 + 631 \times 0.05 + 631 \times 0.05 + 650 \times 0.15$$
$$= 192\,h$$
$$L_{100,5,16\text{N-B}} = 772 \times 0 + 772 \times 0.05 + 772 \times 0.05 + 772 \times 0.05 + 795 \times 0.15$$
$$= 235\,h$$
$$L_{100,5} = L_{100,5,16\text{N-A}} + L_{100,5,16\text{N-B}} = 427\,h$$

4.4.7   *Matching real capacity and expected load*

So far, the following three methods for production load computation have been introduced.

Resource profile for center 100 - assembly shop A								
Week before product delivery								
7	6	5	4	3	2	1	0	
					0.05	0.05		motor assembly
			0.15	0.05				rotor assembly
0	0	0	0.15	0.05	0.05	0.05	0	Total center 100

Resource profile for center 200 - assembly shop B								
Week before product delivery								
7	6	5	4	3	2	1	0	
			0.1	0.2				stator assembly
0	0	0	0.1	0.2	0	0	0	Total center 200

Resource profile for center 300 - injection molding								
Week before product delivery								
7	6	5	4	3	2	1	0	
			0.01	0.01				collector cup manufacturing
0	0	0	0.01	0.01	0	0	0	Total center 300

Resource profile for center 400 - machine shop								
Week before product delivery								
7	6	5	4	3	2	1	0	
	0.15	0.15						shaft machining
0	0.15	0.15	0	0	0	0	0	Total center 400

Resource profile for center 500 - coil winding shop								
Week before product delivery								
7	6	5	4	3	2	1	0	
	0.3	0.1						coil winding
0	0.3	0.1	0	0	0	0	0	Total center 500

Fig. 4.27 Resource profiles for 16N product family.

- CPOF: Capacity Planning using Overall Factor
- BoC: Bill of Capacity
- RP: Resource Profile

After that the expected load is computed, the available resources, i.e. the production capacity, shall be compared with the computed load. The available capacity, CA, depends on various factors inside a company, such as:

- C_{th}: theoretically computed, or known, available capacity;
- τ: availability ratio of the production means (machines, manpower);
- ρ: yield.

The available theoretical capacity is the maximum output theoretically obtainable from a production centre when all factors are 100% met. For example, the theoretical capacity of an assembly shop with 10 employees, working 8 hours a day, 5 days a week and assembling 12 parts per hour per employee would be:

$$C_{th} = 10 \times 8 \times 5 \times 12 = 4800\,parts/week$$

The availability ratio of the production, τ, is the ratio of the effective availability to the theoretical production capacity. In the previous example, it is often observed that the 10 employees of the assembly shop, despite their present time of $40\,h$ per week, are not effectively assembling products during these 40 hour presence time. A part of the presence time is not productive due to breaks, unexpected events, preparatory work, and so on. In practice, the effective availability ratio for manual work, such as an assembly shop, is generally observed to be around 85%, i.e. $\tau = 85\%$.

The yield, ρ, is a factor which represent quantitatively the difference between the actual and assumed production rate. This factor may vary from team to team, and even changes with time following the growing experience of people and their learning curve, the so-called learning effect. Changes in the yield can also result from a continuous improvement program of a company. In the end, ρ can become higher than 1.

Suppose that the team of the assembly shop in our case has a two year experience and that a continuous improvement program is well established in the company. This has led to an increase of the yield from 95% two years ago to 103% today, then $\rho = 103\%$.

We are now able to calculate the effectively available capacity given by:

$$CA = Cth \times \tau \times \rho$$

The effectively available capacity of our 10 people assembly shop will therefore be:

$$CA = 4800 \times 0.85 \times 1.03 = 4202\,parts/week$$

In practice, the values for τ and ρ are regularly adapted (in most cases yearly) on the basis of data acquisitions and analysis.

4.4.8 *Balancing production load and capacity*

As for the aggregate planning, matching production load versus available capacity can be done using three basic strategies: demand following, stable and mixed strategy.

Rough Cut Capacity Planning, RCCP, is used to perform a quick check on a few key resources required to implement the Master Production Schedule. In other words, the RCCP determines the impact of the MPS on the

ʁ-hours, machine hours, purchase volume, and some critical resources.
ɪe RCCP shows that the proposed MPS is not feasible due to insuffi-
ɪ resources, either resources should be reallocated or the MPS should
evised. The reverse situation can also happen, which requires other
ɪions to reduce the unused resources.

Modifying the MPS often leads to anticipating demand by several peri-
ɔds, which entails creating anticipation inventory which increases the stocking costs. Modifying the available capacity can be costly depending on the
flexibility of the production system and the workforce.

4.4.9 *Summary and comparison of rough cut capacity planning*

CPOF: Capacity Planning using Overall Factors

This simple procedure can is found in number of manufacturing firms thanks
to the advantages the method offers, such as ease of calculation (which is
straightforward) and minimal data requirements. Firms can apply this
method since data are often readily available and computation method is
simply to apply. However, the following weaknesses are observed:

- It does not take into account the distribution of production load over
  several periods but assumes that all required production loads are concentrated on the same period, which is, in fact, the referenced MPS
  planning period;
- It does not take into account any variation of the product mix;
- It does not take into account the influence of any production lot size.

BoC: Bill of Capacity

This technique does take into account the actual product mix for each
period. Therefore this method is more suitable for firms which face significant period-to-period product mix variations. However, there are still some
drawbacks with the BoC method:

- It assumes that all production loads affect the production in the same
  period without considering the production load distribution over several
  periods;
- It does not take into account the influence of any production lot size.

RP: Resource Profiles

This method takes into account the timing of required resources. Compared with the CPOF and BoC, it does consider the load distribution over several planning periods covering the production lead-time. The RP method is therefore more accurate when the total production lead-time is larger than one planning period (i.e. ≥ 2 periods). The method requires however more detailed information (the resource profiles of all finished products) and more computational resources. The RP method does not take into account the influence of any production lot size, which might be a drawback of this method.

Figure 4.28 illustrates the differences between the three Rough Cut Capacity Planning methods. It indicates the computed production load on the coil winding production centre 500 of the MotionTech case. It can be observed that CPOF and BoC give almost similar results whereas RP, which takes the lead-time into consideration, gives a different load profile. This is due to the fact that the production lead-time of MotionTech (3 weeks) is larger than the unit of planning period (a week).

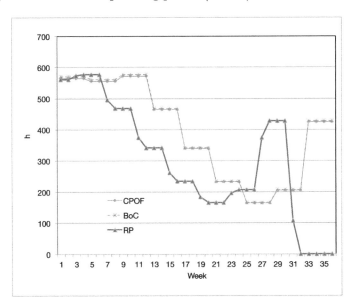

Fig. 4.28   Comparison of the three rough cut capacity planning results — coil winding shop centre 500.

4.5　Detailed planning with material requirement planning

Following the elaboration of the MPS, the next step in the hierarchical production planning deals with the detail material planning. It consists of determining the requirements and the production plans for all the items which compose finished products (from level 1 to the bottom level of the BoM). These requirements are called dependent demands as they are deduced from the finished product demand (the independent demand).

Historically, general inventory management has been used in production management until the beginning of the 1960s. In such a system, the requirement of each item is defined independently of the others, just considering its periodic consumption and the chosen inventory management parameters. Such methodologies can provide a feasible solution to a limited number of items in production, however working under a strong hypothesis, i.e. there are of relatively low volume of items to manage with a reasonably stable demand. If these conditions are no longer satisfied, it can produce poor service and high inventory costs.

The limitations and related difficulties promoted, around 1960, the development of a more effective and sophisticated approach called Material Requirement Planning (MRP). The MRP has been further developed and has become the main company software offered on the market for production planning and control. The extended version is also referred to as Manufacturing Resource Planning (MRP II).

4.5.1　*MRP process and computation*

The understanding of the MRP requires a couple of additional terms and definitions, which are given in Table 4.19.

The MRP method is based on two main concepts:

(1) Time phasing: the division of the planning horizon in constant time buckets (planning periods);
(2) Explosion of requirements: the computation of the gross requirements of a given item from the net requirements of its parent item.

The explosion of requirements is directly dependent on the BoM, which defines the hierarchical relations among items.

The MRP method is an iterative process that proceeds level by level from the top (finished product at level 0) to the bottom of the BoM as illustrated in Fig. 4.29. The processes and methodology presented in this

Table 4.19 Terminologies used in the MRP method.

Term	Symbol	Description
Period	t	Constant time bucket used as a time unit for the whole planning process (for example one week)
Planning horizon	H	Time frame, measured in periods, covered by the planning process
Parent item		Item of the next higher level in the BoM
Child item		Item of the next lower level in the BoM
Gross requirement	GR_t	Initial requirement in one period, not taking into account any on-hand inventory or work in progress
Net requirement	NR_t	Requirement in one period calculated from the gross requirement and taking into account possible on-hand and work in progress
Explosion of requirement		Calculation of the gross requirement of an item from the net requirements of its parent item
Lead-time		Average time lag between the launching of a production order and the receipt of the corresponding items in stock
Launched order	LO_t	Production or purchase order in progress, i.e. that has been launched in the past (before the first period of the planning horizon)
Planned order	PO_t	Production or purchase order defined in the plan but not yet executed
Launched order receipt		Delivery of a launched order, at the beginning of a given period
Planned order receipt		Delivery of a planned order, at the beginning of a given period
Planned order release	OR_t	Launching proposal of a planned order, at the beginning of a given period
Lot sizing		Determination of the lot size according to specific criteria defined in the production or purchasing contract
Projected available balance	SP_t	Quantity of a given item that is anticipated to be available in inventory at the end of a planning period

section are based on the following hypotheses:

- All items are subjected to stock transactions between the different production steps;
- All the components of an item are required when a production order is launched;
- All the components are required in the exact quantity as defined in the BoM;
- Each production order can be executed independently of the others.

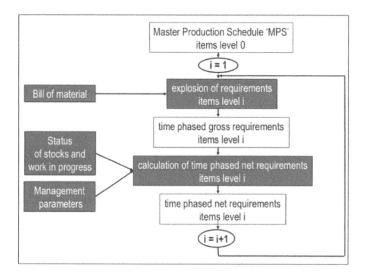

Fig. 4.29   Schematic representation of the MRP method.

Referring to Fig. 4.29, the method starts by receiving the gross requirements from the MPS, i.e. the planned order receipt at level 0 (typically the final assembly). According to the principle of explosion of requirements, the net requirements at level 0, the planned orders PO are used to compute the gross requirements generated at level 1. As for the period of availability, the gross requirements at level 1 must be anticipated considering the lead-time of the operation at level 0 so that the required components should be available at the starting moment of the operation. The target period of the gross requirement at level 1 corresponds to the period of the planned order release at level 0. An example is illustrated in Fig. 4.30 assuming that this center does not have any safety stock policy ($S_s = 0$). The target period of the gross requirement at level $i + 1$ corresponds to the period of the planned order release at level i.

	- Lead-time level 0 (final assembly) = 2 periods											
	- Lot sizing policy level 0: multiple of 30											
	- Lead-time level 1 = 3 periods											
	- Lot sizing policy level 1: multiple of 10											
	Period t		1	2	3	4	5	6	7	8	9	10
level 0	Planned demand PP_t			20		10		10	5		35	10
	Firm orders CO_t			10				20				
	Launched orders LO_t											
	On-hand inventory SP_0		25									
	Proj. available balance SP_t			25	5	5	25	55	35	60	90	85	75
	Planned order receipt PO_t						30	30		30	30	30	
	Planned order release OR_t				30	30		30	30	30			
level 1	Gross requiremnt GR_t				30	30		30	30	30			
	Launched orders LO_t				15	30							
	On-hand inventory SP_0		20										
	Proj. available balance SP_t			20	5	5	5	5	5	5	5	5	5
	Planned order receipt PO_t							30	30	30			
	Planned order release OR_t				30	30	30						

Fig. 4.30   Explosion of requirement from level 0 to level 1.

The gross requirements at level 1 are computed according to the relation:

$$GR_t(i + 1) = c \times OR_t(i), \text{ with } i \geq 0 \tag{4.21}$$

where $GR_t(i+1)$ is the gross requirement at level $i+1$, $OR_t(i)$ the planned order release at level i and c is then number of required child items at level $i + 1$. If the parent item of level i is defined in the BoM, then at level $i + 1$, the net requirement is computed based on the gross requirement and according to the following equations:

$$NR_t(i + 1) = GR_t(i + 1) - SP_{t-1}(i + 1) - LO_t(i + 1) \tag{4.22}$$

$$SP_t(i + 1) = SP_{t-1}(i + 1) + LO_t(i + 1) + PO_t(i + 1) - GR_t(i + 1) \tag{4.23}$$

In Fig. 4.30 for period 6, we have the follow computation examples:

$$GR_6(1) = c \times OR_6(0) = 1 \times 30 = 30 \tag{4.24}$$

$$NR_6(1) = GR_6(1) - SP_5(1) - LO_6(1) = 30 - 5 - 0 = 25 \tag{4.25}$$

As the lot-sizing policy at level 1 calls for a multiple of 15,

$$PO_6(1) = 30$$

The production step requires 3 week lead-time at level 1, therefore the following order release is obtained.

$$OR_3(1) = 30$$

The above-presented procedure shall be applied to all constitutive child items at level $i+1$ so as to establish the full range of MRP covering all the items in the BoM. Once the net requirements of all items at level $i+1$ are computed, the process is iterated and renewed at the next level.

Applying the MRP procedure helps determine production or purchasing order releases for the items. The purchasing of certain types of components may require the forecast of finished products more than half a year in advance. Depending on the forecasting reliability, unreliable forecasts may lead to a lack of components which entails an interruption of the production with late deliveries. Or on the contrary, a high level of inventories due to unreliable forecasting. Such a problem is well known when the MRP method is used in uncertain environments, especially dealing with long lead-times.

The planned order releases will be used later for operating production orders and purchasing activities. It is then necessary to check again, at this detailed planning level, whether the centres still have available capacity. Capacity Requirement Planning (CRP) is a relevant method to apply for that purpose, which is presented in the last subsection of this chapter, after that the MRP is presented.

4.5.2   *Application of the MRP to MotionTech*

Let us first recall the production structure of MotionTech, as it will serve as a basis for the MRP process. The first 12 weeks of the final assembly schedule are given in Fig. 4.31. The planned orders, PO, derived from the MPS should be available at the beginning of the period in which they appear. As the lead-time of motor assembly is 2 weeks, these orders must be released 2 weeks before, as indicated in Frame 1. For example the planned order for assembly of motor 16N-A in week 10 ($PO_{10} = 640\,pcs.$) should be realised in week 8, ($OR_8 = 640\,pcs.$).

The planned order releases of the final assembly schedule constitute the gross requirements for the production steps at level 1; for stator assembly, collector cup manufacturing and rotor assembly, according to the relation in Eq. (4.21). In this case, $c = 1$ since there is one single stator, one single collector cup, and one single rotor for each motor. By applying the equation

Final assembly schedule; projected available balance												
16N-A												
Month		1				2				3		
Week	1	2	3	4	5	6	7	8	9	10	11	12
On-hand inventory 850												
Safety stock 800												
Gross requirement MPS	641	641	641	641	631	631	631	631	650	650	650	650
Proj. avail. balance	829	848	807	806	815	804	813	802	812	802	812	802
Launched orders	620	660										
Planned order receipt			600	640	640	620	640	620	660	640	660	640
Planned order release	600	640	640	620	640	620	660	640	660	640	540	520
16N-B												
Month		1				2				3		
Week	1	2	3	4	5	6	7	8	9	10	11	12
On-hand inventory 1035												
Safety stock 1000												
Gross requirement MPS	783	783	783	783	772	772	772	772	795	795	795	795
Proj. avail. balance	1052	1069	1006	1003	1011	1019	1007	1015	1000	1005	1010	1015
Launched orders	800	800										
Planned order receipt			720	780	780	780	760	780	780	800	800	800
Planned order release	720	780	780	780	760	780	780	800	800	800	640	640

Fig. 4.31 Final assembly schedule for products 16N-A and 16N-B.

to all periods and for the two motors 16N-A and 16N-B, we can compute the gross requirements for stator assembly, collector cup manufacturing, and rotor assembly. For the sake of simplicity, we will consider only rotor assembly here. The results of the computation are provided in Fig. 4.32.

Let us consider period 10 and product 16N-A. Since the planned order release for the motor assembly is 640 (in Fig. 4.31), the gross requirement for rotor assembly in week 10 is also 640 (shown in Fig. 4.32). The projected available balance at the end of the previous period (week 9) is 420, the safety stock requirement is 400, and the lot-sizing policy requires production in batch of multiple 50. The net requirement for week 10 is the computed according to the following way, given that there is no launched order:

$$NR_{10} = GR_{10} + Ss - SP_9 = 640 + 400 - 420 = 620$$

Due to the defined lot-sizing policy (multiple of 50) with the 2 week lead-time in rotor assembly, this leads to the following planned order and planned order release.

$$PO_{10} = 650, \quad OR_8 = 650$$

Then, the projected available balance for week 10 is computed as:

$$SP_{10} = SP_9 + PO_{10} - GR_{10} = 420 + 650 - 640 = 430$$

With the obtained results at level 1, we can proceed, in a similar way, going through the lower level, level 2 for shaft machining and coil winding.

	On-hand inventory & safety stock, rotor assembly				Lot-sizing policy, rotor assembly				
	On-hand		Safety stock		16N-A	min.	50	multiple of	50
16N-A	450		400		16N-B	min.	50	multiple of	50
16N-B	625		500		Launched orders, rotor assembly				
					Week	1	2	3	4	5
					16N-A	620	620			
					16N-B	700	700			

Production schedule rotor assembly

16N-A

	Month	1				2				3			
	Week	1	2	3	4	5	6	7	8	9	10	11	12
On-hand inventory	450												
Safety stock	400												
Gross requirement MPS		600	640	640	620	640	620	660	640	660	640	540	520
Proj. avail. balance		470	450	410	440	400	430	420	430	420	430	440	420
Launched orders		620	620										
Planned order receipt				600	650	600	650	650	650	650	650	550	500
Planned order release		600	650	600	650	650	650	650	650	550	500	500	550

16N-B

	Month	1				2				3			
	Week	1	2	3	4	5	6	7	8	9	10	11	12
On-hand inventory	625												
Safety stock	500												
Gross requirement MPS		720	780	780	780	760	780	780	800	800	800	640	640
Proj. avail. balance		605	525	545	515	505	525	545	545	545	545	505	515
Launched orders		700	700										
Planned order receipt				800	750	750	800	800	800	800	800	600	650
Planned order release		800	750	750	800	800	800	800	800	600	650	650	650

Fig. 4.32   Production schedule for rotor assembly for products 16N-A and 16N-B.

We assume here that the two rotors use the same shaft, different coils, but the same copper wire to produce the coil, according to the BoM. We assume as well that the coil for rotor 16N-A requires $35\,m$ of copper wire, while the coil for rotor 16N-B requires $42\,m$.

The computation of the gross requirements, net requirements, planned orders, and projected available balance proceeds similarly as for the rotor assembly. The obtained results are provided in Fig. 4.33.

Here is the example computation. The planned order release for the rotor assembly is 500, thus the gross requirement for coil winding in week 10 is also 500. The projected available balance at the end of the previous period (week 9) is 1280, the safety stock requirement is 1200, and the lot-sizing policy calls for batches of multiple 100 and minimum 500. The net requirement for week 10 is thus:

$$NR_{10} = GR_{10} + Ss - SP_9 = 500 + 1200 - 1280 = 420$$

		On-hand inventory & safety stock, coil winding			Lot-sizing policy, coil winding					
		On-hand		Safety stock	16N-A	min.	500	multiple of	100	
	16N-A	1230		1200	16N-B	min.	500	multiple of	100	
	16N-B	1640		1600	Launched orders, coil winding					
					Week	1	2	3	4	5
					16N-A	700	700			
					16N-B	800	800			

Production schedule coil winding

16N-A

	Month	1				2				3			
	Week	1	2	3	4	5	6	7	8	9	10	11	12
On-hand inventory 1230													
Safety stock 1200													
Gross requirement MPS		600	650	600	650	650	650	650	650	550	500	500	550
Proj. avail. balance		1330	1380	1280	1230	1280	1230	1280	1230	1280	1280	1280	1230
Launched orders		700	700										
Planned order receipt				500	600	700	600	700	600	600	500	500	500
Planned order release		500	600	700	600	700	600	600	500	500	500	500	500

16N-B

	Month	1				2				3			
	Week	1	2	3	4	5	6	7	8	9	10	11	12
On-hand inventory 1640													
Safety stock 1600													
Gross requirement MPS		800	750	750	800	800	800	800	800	600	650	650	650
Proj. avail. balance		1640	1690	1640	1640	1640	1640	1640	1640	1640	1690	1640	1690
Launched orders		800	800										
Planned order receipt				700	800	800	800	800	800	600	700	600	700
Planned order release		700	800	800	800	800	800	600	700	600	700	500	500

Fig. 4.33 Production schedule coil winding for products 16N-A and 16N-B.

Due to the defined lot-sizing policy and the 2-week lead-time for the supply in coil winding, this leads to

$$PO_{10} = 500 \quad \text{and} \quad OR_8 = 500$$

And the projected available balance for week 10 is:

$$SP_{10} = SP_9 + PO_{10} - GR_{10} = 1280 + 500 - 500 = 1280$$

Based on the planned orders for coil winding, let us compute the requirements for the copper wire that should be purchased from suppliers. As the two coils use the same type of copper wire, we have to add the net requirements from these two coils to compute the gross requirements for the copper wire. Recall also that the coil for rotor 16N-A requires $35\,m$ of copper wire, whereas the coil for rotor 16N-B requires $42\,m$. The computation of the gross requirements, net requirements, planned orders and projected available balance follows a similar method as for the previous production steps, but with the addition of the net requirements of the two coils. The obtained results are provided in Fig. 4.34.

	On-hand inventory & safety stock, copper wire (km)			Lot-sizing policy, copper wire (km)					
	On-hand		Safety stock	16N	min.	100	multiple of	50	
16N	250		200	Launched orders, copper wire (km)					
				Week	1	2	3	4	5
				16N	100	0	150		

Purchase schedule copper wire (km)

16N

		Month		1				2				3		
		Week	1	2	3	4	5	6	7	8	9	10	11	12
On-hand inventory	250													
Safety stock	200													
Gross requirement MPS			46.9	54.6	58.1	54.6	58.1	54.6	46.2	46.9	42.7	46.9	38.5	38.5
Proj. avail. balance			303.1	248.5	340.4	285.8	227.7	273.1	226.9	280	237.3	290.4	251.9	213.4
Launched orders			100	0	150									
Planned order receipt						0	0	100	0	100	0	100	0	0
Planned order release			0	0	100	0	100	0	100	0	0	100	0	0

Fig. 4.34   Purchase schedule copper wire for products 16N-A and 16N-B.

In order to understand the computation details, let us consider the situation in period 10. The planned order releases for the coil winding are 500 for coil 16N-A and 700 for coil 16N-B, thus the gross requirement for copper wire in week 10 is:

$$GR_{10} = 500 \times 35 + 700 \times 42 = 46900\,m = 46.9\,km$$

The projected available balance at the end of the previous period (week 9) is $237.3\,km$ and the safety stock requirement is $200\,km$. Furthermore, the lot-sizing policy calls for batches of multiple 50 km with minimum 100 km. The net requirement for week 10 is thus:

$$NR_{10} = GR_{10} + Ss - SP_9 = 46.9 + 200 - 237.3 = 9.6\,km$$

Due to the defined lot-sizing policy and the 3-week lead-time for the supply of the copper wire, this leads to

$$PO_{10} = 100 \quad \text{and} \quad OR_7 = 100$$

And the projected available balance for week 10 is:

$$SP_{10} = SP_9 + PO_{10} - GR_{10} = 237.3 + 100 - 46.9 = 290.4\,km$$

The above-described MRP processes for rotor assembly, coil winding machining, and copper wire purchase shall be applied to all items of the BoM of all finished products. Each single computation might be simple, but the large number of items makes the whole process highly complex.

4.5.3 *Capacity requirement planning and the MRP*

This section introduces Capacity Requirement Planning (CRP) which uses the results of the MRP process for the purpose of verifying the load and capacity at the detailed level. The following list shows the input data and output of CRP.

Input data for the CRP method

(1) Launched orders in the production (WIP) and their current status;
(2) Planned orders calculated by the MRP;
(3) Inventory level;
(4) Item routings;
(5) Standard time per unit for each operation and each production centre of the routing.

Output from the CRP method

(1) Labour resource requirements for each production centre;
(2) Machine resource requirements for each production centre;
(3) Purchasing volume.

	Lot sizes	Operation	Production center	Standard setup time [hours]	Standard setup time/piece [hours]*	Standard run time/piece [hours]	Total time/piece [hours]*
Finished product							
A	40	1 of 1	100	1.0	0.025	0.025	0.05
B	20	1 of 1	100	1.0	0.050	1.250	1.30
Component							
C	40	1 of 2	200	1.0	0.025	0.575	0.60
		2 of 2	300	1.0	0.025	0.175	0.20
D	60	1 of 1	200	2.0	0.033	0.167	0.20
E	100	1 of 1	200	2.0	0.020	0.080	0.10
F	100	1 of 1	200	2.0	0.020	0.0425	0.0625

* assuming constant lot size

Fig. 4.35 Example of routing and standard time data for CRP.

The data are composed of period-dependent data (launched orders, planned orders, inventory level) and period-independent data (item routing, standard time per unit). Launched orders and planned orders in the MRP system are inputs to CRP, which, through the use of routings and time standards, translates these orders into labour and machine hours for each production centre and by planning period. Consequently, the CRP allows finding an acceptable solution between required versus available resources, taking into account the requirement of each item, the status of inventories and work in progress, as well as a possible lot sizing policy.

Implementing CRP requires both detailed industrial engineering databases (e.g. work standards, routing files) and formal systems for handling transactions on the shop-floor. Figure 4.35 gives a typical data example of the routing and standard time that are required for applying the CRP method.

Going through the level-by-level planning with the corresponding capacity planning, it is possible to detect a capacity problem at the detailed level even though Rough-Cut Capacity Planning of higher level may indicate sufficient capacity to execute the MPS. The CRP method is capable of detecting such a case concerning particular planning periods and production centres.

Characteristics and procedure for capacity requirement planning

The CRP procedure is closely related to the MRP computation of the time-phased net requirements. Here are some characteristics of the CRP.

(1) The CRP is based on the information produced by the explosion process of the MRP, which includes the consideration of lot size, as well as the lead-times for both launched orders (scheduled receipts) and planned orders.
(2) The gross to net calculation of an MRP system takes into account the items already stored in the form of inventories of both components and assembled items.
(3) The shop-floor control system accounts for the current status of launched orders so that only the resources needed to complete the remaining work on launched orders causes the production load.
(4) CRP takes into account other independent demands, such as service parts and any additional resources that might be required by MRP planners reacting to scrap, item record errors, etc.

For each planning period t and for each production centre i, the load $L_{i,t}$ is calculated using the following equation:

$$L_{i,t} = \sum_{PO_i} \left(t_{i,j}^m + n_j t_{i,j}^0 \right) \tag{4.26}$$

with:

- $L_{i,t}$ = production load on centre i for period t
- PO_i = production orders to be executed during period t in centre i
- $t_{i,j}^m$ = set-up time of centre i for item j
- $t_{i,j}^0$ = run time of item j in centre i
- n_j = number of items j in production order

Application of the CRP to MotionTech

Let us focus on production centre 300-injection moulding, which works on the collector cup manufacturing. To apply the CRP method, we first need to know the complete schedule of production centre 300 resulting from the MRP process. This schedule is provided in Fig. 4.36.

We then need to know the standard times in production centre 300. The corresponding data are given in Fig. 4.37.

Recall that the Resource Profiles of production centre 300 in Section 4.4.7 indicated a workload of $0.02\,h/pcs.$, which is coherent with the CRP-data. With the data from Figs. 4.36 and 4.37, we can now compute the load on production centre 300 by applying Eq. (4.26). The results are given in Fig. 4.38, together with those of the RP computation.

Let us consider the situation in period 7 as a computation example. The planned order releases in this week are 0 for the collector cup 16N-A and 2500 for collector cup 16N-B. Thus the production load is computed as below.

$$L_{300,12} = (t_{300,16\text{N-A}}^m + n_{16\text{N-A}} \times t_{300,16\text{N-A}}^0) + (t_{300,16\text{N-B}}^m + n_{16\text{N-B}} \times t_{300,16\text{N-B}}^0)$$

$$L_{300,12} = 2 + 2500 \times 0.02 = 52\,h$$

The results of the CRP versus RP methods are compared in Fig. 4.39.

Even though the average load per week is almost identical, the distribution of the computed load using both methods is quite different. This is due to the fact that the load profile computed with the RP is derived from the MPS on level 0, without taking into account the lot-sizing policies at all levels of the BoM. On the contrary, the CRP method derives the load

On-hand inventory & safety stock, collector cup manufacturing			Lot-sizing policy, collector cup			
	On-hand	Safety stock	16N-A	min. 2500 multiple of		500
16N-A	2550	2000	16N-B	min. 2500 multiple of		500
16N-B	4400	3000	Launched orders, collector cup			
			Week	1	2 3 4 5	
			16N-A	3000	0	
			16N-B	0	3000	

MRP, collector cup manufacturing

16N-A

	Month	1				2				3			
	Week	1	2	3	4	5	6	7	8	9	10	11	12
On-hand inventory 2550													
Safety stock 2000													
Gross requirement MPS		600	640	640	620	640	620	660	640	660	640	540	520
Proj. avail. balance		4950	4310	3670	3050	2410	4290	3630	2990	2330	4190	3650	3130
Launched orders		3000											
Planned order				0	0	0	2500	0	0	0	2500	0	0
Planned order release		0	0	0	2500	0	0	0	2500	0	0	0	0

16N-B

	Month	1				2				3			
	Week	1	2	3	4	5	6	7	8	9	10	11	12
On-hand inventory 4400													
Safety stock 3000													
Gross requirement MPS		720	780	780	780	760	780	780	800	800	800	640	640
Proj. avail. balance		3680	5900	5120	4340	3580	5300	4520	3720	5420	4620	3980	3340
Launched orders			3000										
Planned order				0	0	0	2500	0	0	2500	0	0	0
Planned order release		0	0	0	2500	0	0	2500	0	0	0	2500	0

Fig. 4.36   Production schedule collector cup manufacturing for products 16N-A and 16N-B.

Standard time data for collector cup manufacturing							
	Lot size	operation	Production center	Standard set-up (h)	Standard set-up/pcs. (h)	Standard run-time/pcs. (h)	Total time/pcs. (h)
16N-A	2500	1 of 1	300 - inj. molding	2	0.0008	0.02	0.0208
16N-B	2500	1 of 1	300 - inj. molding	2	0.0008	0.02	0.0208

Fig. 4.37   Standard time for production centre 300-injection moulding.

from the actual planned orders at the considered centre level. It includes also the lot-sizing policies in the production centre, as well as that of all the upper levels.

CRP involves a complex process requiring more detailed information. It should be used when more accurate results are really necessary, i.e. for selected critical resources. Therefore the identification of these critical resources should precede the application of the CRP, some of which are given below.

Load on collector cup manufacturing using CRP and resource profile													
CRP													
	Month	1				2				3			
	Week	1	2	3	4	5	6	7	8	9	10	11	12
Order release 16N-A		0	0	0	2500	0	0	0	2500	0	0	0	0
Order release 16N-B		0	0	0	2500	0	0	2500	0	0	0	2500	0
Load (h)		0	0	0	104	0	0	52	52	0	0	52	0
Resource profile													
	Month	1				2				3			
	Week	1	2	3	4	5	6	7	8	9	10	11	12
Load (h) 16N-A		13	12.62	12.62	12.62	12.81	13	13	13	11.77	10.54	10.54	10.54
Load (h) 16N-b		16	15.44	15.44	15.44	15.67	15.9	15.9	15.9	14.39	12.88	12.88	12.88
Load (h)		28	28.06	28.06	28.06	28.48	28.9	28.9	28.9	26.16	23.42	23.42	23.42

Fig. 4.38   Load on production centre 300-injection computed by CRP and RP.

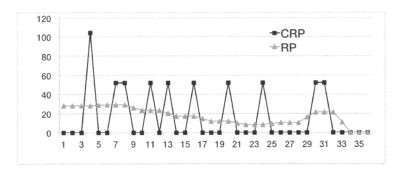

Fig. 4.39   Comparison of the production load on centre 300 determined using CRP and RP.

- bottleneck production centres
- suppliers with limited capacity
- single machines critical for the production process
- specific human resources with critical competencies

Another important issue deals with choosing the most appropriate unit of measurement with regards to the chosen key resource, for instance, people capacity (hour, person, person-year, and so on), machine capacity (hour, ton, km, m^2).

As discussed with the Rough Cut Capacity Planning methods, the adaptations of the load and/or the capacity may be required in order to obtain an optimal balance between them.

4.6 Coaching guideline and suggested assignment

In this chapter, we have discussed level-by-level processes of manufacturing operations planning. At each level, suitable methods of capacity planning are also presented.

The following subsections present example assignments extracted from our coaching sessions.

4.6.1 *First week — Learning basic concepts*

The objectives of this coaching session are:

- To understand the procedure for generating a feasible Aggregate Production Plan.
- To identify the set of data required for that purpose.
- To establish your company's Aggregate Production Plan of one product family over a 12 month horizon starting in October.

Task list

- Discuss with your team members what will be your management strategy for the purpose of finding an optimal solution between the market demand and the internal production capacity (the availability of labours).
- When you receive the company's productivity data from your coach, check them with respect to the requirement for generating a feasible AP as well as the liquidity profile (cash inputs and outputs).
- Create a feasible Aggregate Production Plan (AP) for one product family of your choice (you will do it later for all product families); a feasible AP should fulfil the market requirements defined by the forecasts at minimum cost, while respecting the constraints of the enterprise and its operations environment.
- Review the methodology and procedure for generating the AP and computing the cash-in and cash-out evolution.

Preparatory discussion

Please check the following points.

- Discuss with your coach how to compute the cash flow of your company, which should be demonstrated during your intermediary presentation.
- Identify the data required for your MPS generation and request missing data.

4.6.2 Second week — Intermediary presentation

The goal is to establish the first phase of the hierarchical planning process, i.e. the generation of a feasible Aggregate Plan and MPS.

Tasks to complete

- Present your Aggregate Production Plan.
- Draw a graphical representation of the evolution of the cash-in and -out for the same product family based on your Aggregate Production Plan.
- Generate a feasible Master Production Schedule for a specific product family over a 12-month horizon starting in October. Your input data should be summarised.
- Comment the obtained results and methodology.
- Present your purchasing plan according to the established plan.

Presentation contents

Provide your data in the form of clearly documented Excel sheets. Prepare a PowerPoint presentation of your results in putting forward the most significant points (hypothesis, methods, difficulties, results).

Preparatory discussion

- The choice of a specific manufacturing centre and the characteristics of manufacturing processes.
- To understand the procedure for generating MRP.

4.6.3 Third week — Consolidating the whole concepts

Your objectives for this coaching session are:

- To generate the MRP from the MPS.

- To understand the procedure for comparing the load profiles on a specific production centre obtained.
- Compute the Rough Cut Capacity Planning.

Your task for this coaching session

- List the data you require for computing the load profile using Capacity Requirement Planning.
- Describe the methodology and procedure you intend to use to compute a purchasing plan for specific components over a 12 month horizon starting in October.
- Generate your MRP.
- Discuss the methodology and procedure to compute the load profile of a specific production centre.
- Compute the Capacity Requirement Planning of one of your work centres.
- Depending on your progress, you can also try to compute the Capacity Requirement Planning and verify the result with your coach.

Chapter 5

Inventory Management

5.1 Introduction

Inventory Management is one of the key issues for the efficient management of manufacturing firms. A central purpose of inventory is to enable quick and reliable delivery of finished products to clients. However, the downside of inventory is its high cost. This chapter illustrates the foundations of inventory management with its role in manufacturing firms. The purpose of having different types of inventory is discussed and their trade-offs are highlighted. The discussion will be followed by listing all associated costs of inventory management which serve as criteria to evaluate the inventory management policies. Finally, mathematical models will be explained which can be used as decision making tools for the dimensioning of inventories.

Inventory management is a complex management issue that takes many forms in different organisations. Although concepts and basic dynamics hold in many industries, it is possible that the application of certain inventory management can lead to completely different result of operations. Therefore the methods and tools should be used after companies have understood clearly the assumptions and their limitations. Appropriate inventory policies can support smooth material flow, both on the shop floor and in the distribution network. However, an optimal inventory policy requires an alignment with all partners in the value-adding network from suppliers to the end customers. Inventory policies are central to the understanding of current production paradigms such as Lean Manufacturing, Quick Response Manufacturing, Total Quality Management or Material Requirement Planning systems.

The chapter begins by presenting basic concepts of inventory management. Key vocabulary and fundamental problems are explained in the subsections which follow. Section 4 presents the cost modelling used in inventory management. It is based on the Economic Order Quantity (EOQ) model, which is one of the oldest, but still most commonly used models for inventory management. Its purpose and limiting assumptions will be discussed, followed by a presentation of various costs of holding inventory. A special emphasis will be given to the logic of the model and assumptions, in order to properly adapt it to different manufacturing environments. In Section 5, various inventory management methods are presented conceptually with example illustrations. This section tries to explain how to differentiate the various methods based on their respective hypotheses, fields of applications, strengths and weaknesses. Section 6 deals with the critical issues of uncertainty and how to cope with it. This is an important issue since one of the main purposes of maintaining inventories is to guarantee customer service level within an uncertain environment. In Section 7, the methodologies and statistical models used for calculating safety stocks are presented.

5.2   Basic concepts and definitions

Inventory refers to the amount of goods that is held at some location in a value adding network. It could take the form of raw material, parts, components or finished products.

Various types of inventories can be found within a firm and can be classified into stock or WIP.

- Stock: bound, identified materials outside of any operations processes.
- WIP: Work In Progress, usually not identified.
- Inventory: sum of stock and WIP.

Both stocks and WIP can be located at different stages within the production system. For example, stock can be located at several locations within a firm or a group of companies. It can be found amongst the network of production resources (machinery, workstations, assembly lines, factories, etc.) and within the logistics resources (material handling systems, transportation resources, warehouses, retailers, etc.).

5.2.1 *Types of stock*

Stocks can be classified according to different criteria. Three classifications are presented below:

(1) Classification according to the objectives of the stock;
(2) Classification according to the level of the stored items;
(3) Classification according to the stock location.

5.2.1.1 *Classification according to the objectives of the stock*

There are many purposes for having stock in a production network. Although each type of stock has its own objective, they must be managed as a whole to assure efficient and smooth production. Table 5.1 lists the types of stock and their main objectives.

Table 5.1   Stock types and corresponding objective.

Type of stock	Main objective
Safety stock	Facing uncertainties
Batch production stock	Reducing production cost
Buffer stock	Decoupling successive processes
Anticipation stock	Covering irregular requirements
Transit stock	Covering transport time

5.2.1.2 *Classification according to the item level*

Stocks can alternatively be classified according to the level in the Bill of Material of the stored item, which is related to their position in the production process. For instance, before any production operation has begun, the stock is mainly constituted of raw materials or components bought from suppliers. It is referred to as "stock of raw material or component". Figure 5.1 illustrates the identification of stocks according to the BoM level criterion.

5.2.1.3 *Classification according to the location*

An important element to consider in inventory management is the location of stock. The stock management parameters cannot be determined without considering their location since location affects the required stock level. Let us consider a simple example. Suppose a firm producing in Europe sells

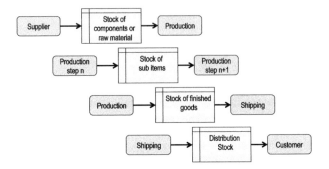

Fig. 5.1   Classification according to their position in the manufacturing process (BoM level).

some finished products in Japan. Two different stock management strategies can be chosen: stocking finished products in a warehouse in Japan, i.e. close to the market, or stocking them in Europe, i.e.close to the factory. According to the chosen strategy, the requirement of stock levels of these two stocks might be quite different to serve the Japanese market. Stock location decisions must be made at different production positions in the value-adding network. From the factory floor to warehouses distributed worldwide, there might be several options of locating stock. Here, two main issues shall be addressed: (1) centralisation versus de-centralisation; and (2) stock item of a single BoM level versus stock mix. Figure 5.2 illustrates different types of stock according to this classification.

Centralisation versus de-centralisation

Centralisation means that different stocks are concentrated in one single area. In an extreme situation, all items needed by any production centre would be delivered from the same centralised stock location. The main advantage is to save storage costs by sharing resources such as warehouses, racks, material handling equipment, and so on. The main disadvantages are the increase in transportation cost from the centralised stock location to the many production centres as well as the increase in lead-time. The opposite strategy consists of using many small stocking areas, close to each production centre according to their specific requirement. Intermediate stocking strategies can also be chosen in between the opposite cases, i.e. full centralisation and total de-centralisation.

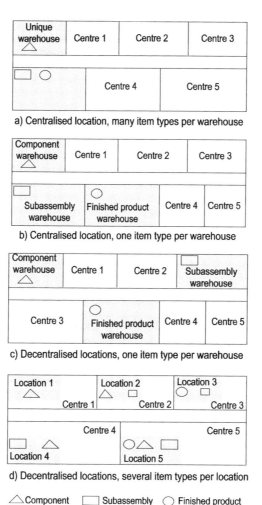

Fig. 5.2 Example of stock location strategies.

Single BoM level versus stock mix, or mixed stock

Stock mix refers that different types of items are stored in a single stocking area. Stocking strategies can vary in such a case from having only one item type (for example, finished products) to having many item types (for instance, components, sub-assemblies and finished products) stored at a specific location. Having different items of different BoM levels in a single stock location, it is more efficient to supply different production centres. However it requires more investment and also leads to higher transportation costs. The following list illustrates commonly found strategies of how to determine stock location.

(a) Centralised stock location with many item types in a single warehouse;
(b) Centralised stock location with only one item type per warehouse;
(c) Decentralised stock locations with only one item type per warehouse;
(d) Decentralised stock locations with several item types per location;
(e) Shop floor storage where each type of item is stored within the production centre, on the shop floor.

Beside the three criteria described above, there are other criteria of stock classification. For example, it is quite common to identify stocks according to their role such as safety stock or anticipation stock. It is be noticed that the classification is not exclusive but composable so that one could define an anticipation, decentralised component stock for instance.

5.2.2 *Purpose and importance of stocks*

The objective of stock management is to determine the ideal level of stocks for achieving the performance goals of a value-adding network. Often, this involves determining the stock levels that will fulfil the service criteria while minimising inventory carrying costs. Management must determine the appropriate trade-off between the cost of stocks and the service level with regards to delay and reliability of order deliveries. It is important to remember that holding inventory is not an activity that adds value to a product but it is rather a means to improve service to customers. If customers were willing to wait long enough for a product, which is the case with highly customised products, then there would be no need for inventory. Inventory in such a case would simply add unnecessary costs.

The key issue lies in understanding the relationship between the capacity of a firm, production delay, and delivery delay. For instance, if a firm has a production cycle shorter than its delivery delay, then it could produce products as they are ordered (Make-To-Order) within the promised delivery delay. Consequently, it would not require stock of finished products to fulfil customer's orders. However, orders often arrive in large quantities and firms have limited capacity, even if they could produce small quantities rapidly. If the firm's capacity is large enough to handle demand peaks, inventory would not be necessary. The reality is that most firms are not in this situation. In today's economy, demand varies significantly and customers request very short delivery delays. In such a highly competitive market situation, it is required for managers to deal with a difficult task. They must have a minimal amount of stock, which is strategically placed in the value adding network, to satisfy the customer service. If the stock levels are too low, delivery delays will increase. If they are too high, inventory costs will increase. There are many factors that will affect the strategy of the inventory manager including the context of the firm, stakeholder interests, production philosophy, and performance measures.

5.3 Financial constitutive elements

The management of inventories is related to at least the three types of costs:

- Inventory carrying cost;
- Ordering cost;
- Shortage and customer service cost.

Inventory management optimisation involves minimising the above-mentioned costs while satisfying the service objectives of the firm. Again, it is important to note that these costs do not add any value to the goods. They have strong influence on management strategies which determine the required performance levels so as to capture a specific portion of a market segment.

5.3.1 *Inventory carrying cost*

Inventory carrying costs are often calculated on the basis of a percentage of the immobilised capital represented by the value of the stored items. The longer the items are held in stock and thus not sold, the longer a firm must continue paying the cost relative to the inventory. These percentages will vary depending on the types of stored items. For example, smaller expensive products such as jewellery will be treated differently than larger inexpensive products. For most products, the annual rate will vary from 15% to 30%. Three main sources of these costs are indicated as follows with the corresponding approximation percentage.

(1) Cost of immobilised capital (approximately 5 to 10%), determined from:

(a) Interest for capital load
(b) Interest of short term placement
(c) ROI (return on investment)

(2) Cost for financing, building or renting and maintaining warehouses (approximately 5 to 10%), including:

(a) Mortgage, rent
(b) Insurance
(c) Maintenance costs, climate control, cleaning, security, and so on
(d) Material handling equipment and other indirect costs

(3) Cost for protecting the stock and obsolescence cost (approximately 5 to 10%).

The inventory carrying cost comprises all the costs associated to having goods in stock. These costs include: mortgage, physical stocking systems (racks, lifts, and conveyors), system software, storage area, administrative salaries. These costs are often accounted for as a ratio of the value of goods stored, but they can also be calculated explicitly.

5.3.2 *Ordering cost*

Ordering cost, also known as transactional cost, encompasses the costs of placing an order of any item such as raw material or components used for production, or launching a production order for internal execution. Placing an order involves many more activities than appears at first glance, especially in organisations that have no integrated modern information technology systems. Some of the common activities include: determining what and how much to order, communicating with the supplier(s) and receiving a quote, receiving ordered items, handling ordered items in the stocking area, creating the bills and receipts, and verifying incoming orders, and so on. These activities require considerable personnel time and material resources. Ordering costs can be classified in the following way:

(a) Ordering administrative costs

- Preparation, control, follow-up and classification of documents;
- Follow-up of delivery;
- Follow-up of accounting.

(b) Transportation cost (may be assumed by vendor)

- Transportation costs;

- Customs;
- Transportation insurance.

(c) Setup cost in production

- Changing tools;
- Changing software programs;
- Machine warm up;
- Insuring process control.

It must be noted that all constitutive cost elements of the ordering cost are independent of the ordered quantity, but fixed costs.

5.3.3 *Shortage and customer service cost*

As mentioned earlier, the main purpose of inventory is to assure supply to productions so as to satisfy required service level to customers. Inventory can be seen as stored capacity that is used to satisfy promised delivery lead-time to customers. So one could consider that shortage and customer service costs are not only related to inventory but also to the firm's capacity.

In countries such as Switzerland where land is very expensive and interest for capital loan relatively low, it may be more economical to have higher levels of resources and little inventory that requires expensive floor space. Consequently, the main question to answer is: what is the cost of not having the appropriate level of capacity to fulfil customer service requirements?

Even though firms might be able to identify several cost elements of shortage and customer service, it is in general difficult to quantify them. Consequently, considering the techniques used to evaluate or estimate these costs, a wide range of variations is observed amongst firms. Some firms simply see customer service as a condition to be satisfied in order to compete, and hence don't measure the real associated costs. The following example shows a set of quantifiable cost elements:

- Customer penalties for late deliveries;
- Express shipment for sending back orders;
- Cancelled orders resulting in profit and material loss;
- Losing the annual business of a client to competitors.

Some cost elements difficult to quantify are:

- Having a (bad) reputation of not delivering on time;
- Catch-up production causing disorder on the shop floor;
- Indirect overtime or outsourcing to support production.

5.4   Cost modelling

The goal of cost modelling is to develop mathematical relations between the cost elements in order to determine quantitative parameters of inventory management. The most common model used by firms today is the Economic Order Quantity (EOQ) function, which was developed in the early 1900s. Although there is much debate on its effectiveness, it definitely helps understanding the main trade-offs involved in inventory management. Essentially, the EOQ function represents a trade-off between the two cost types: ordering cost and inventory carrying cost. We will first begin by stating the assumptions of the EOQ model.

5.4.1   *Economic order quantity (EOQ)*

Assumptions of the EOQ model

The EOQ model is built on the following assumptions:

(1) Demand is constant over time (constant demand rate): it can be represented by a straight line in a quantity versus time graph.
(2) Instantaneous replenishment: there is unlimited capacity and the entire lot is produced (delivered) instantaneously.
(3) Fixed price: price per item does not vary with quantity ordered.
(4) Fixed setup and order placement costs: ordering cost is independent of the lot size and of the status of the factory.
(5) Items are independent from each other, which satisfies one of the following conditions: either there is a single item or there are multiple items which can be considered separately from each other.

Understanding these hypotheses is important for using appropriately the EOQ model. Despite such restrictive assumptions, the EOQ model provides in general good estimation in many real situations.

Composition of the cost in EOQ

The Economic Order Quantity model is proposed in order to formally determine the order quantity decision. The optimisation of the order quantity, Q, is achieved by minimising the total cost of delivery for a given quantity of items, i.e. needs N. The total cost is composed of three elements which are presented below.

1. Purchasing cost

The purchasing cost is the cost paid to a supplier for acquiring the total quantity N of items or for producing it internally. It depends on the number of purchased items N and on the unit price of these items p (Eq. (5.1)).

$$C_{\text{purchase}} = Np \qquad (5.1)$$

In this equation, a strong assumption is given that the unit price is independent of the order quantity. Therefore the total purchasing cost is linearly proportional to the number of items, whereas in real-world procurement it is often possible to purchase a huge amount of items for a relatively lower unit price.

2. Inventory carrying cost

The inventory carrying cost depends on the average stock level $Q/2$, the unit price p and the inventory carrying cost rate r_c. The inventory carrying cost rate r_s is the cost rate for keeping one unit of item in inventory during the considered time horizon (the same period during which the amount of need, N, is estimated). C_y is the annual inventory carrying cost rate of keeping one unit of item in inventory (horizon of one year), which is in general a known value by each enterprise. Subsequently, for the purpose of computing the inventory carrying cost rate for any other horizon, it should be recomputed accordingly. For example, the following formula shows how to compute r_c of 1 month applying the annual inventory carrying cost rate $C_y = 18\%$.

$$r_c \text{ of 1 month} = \frac{C_y}{12} = \frac{0.18}{12} = 0.015 = 1.5\%$$

The average quantity of items in stock is assumed to be half of the order quantity (i.e. $Q/2$) as the demand rate is supposed to be constant.

$$C_{carrying} = \frac{Q}{2} p r_c \qquad (5.2)$$

Note that the inventory carrying cost is linearly dependant on the order quantity.

3. Ordering cost

The ordering cost is a fixed amount L occurring once for each order place-ment. The total ordering cost over the considered time horizon is therefore proportional to the number of orders placed during this time horizon, i.e. to N/Q

$$C_{order} = \frac{N}{Q}L \tag{5.3}$$

Note that the ordering cost is inversely proportional to the order quantity.

4. Total cost

The total cost C_{total} is the sum of these three cost components $C_{purchase} + C_{carrying} + C_{order}$

$$C_{total} = Np + \frac{Q}{2}pr_c + \frac{N}{Q}L \tag{5.4}$$

with:
C_{total} = total cost over the considered time horizon
N = total item need over the considered time horizon
p = unit price or cost
Q = order quantity
r_c = inventory carrying cost rate
L = ordering cost.

Figure 5.3 illustrates the dependence of the three cost components on the order quantity Q.

Trade-off between order and inventory carrying costs

The EOQ function shows the relationship between the total cost C_{total} and the order quantity Q. The objective is to determine the order quantity that will lead the minimum total cost. This quantity is called the Economic Order Quantity Q_e. Referring to Fig. 5.3, the minimum cost corresponds to the lowest point of the total cost curve. It is noticed that this is where the line for the carrying cost and the curve for the ordering cost intersect. The purchase cost does not affect the minimum cost since it is independent of

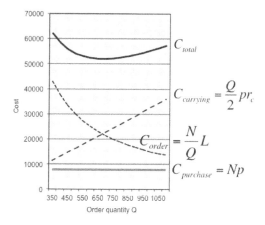

Fig. 5.3   Dependence of the cost components on the order quantity.

Q. Mathematically, this minimum point can be found by deriving the total cost function in terms of Q and setting it to zero. Finally, the expression for the Economic Order Quantity is defined as follows:

$$Q_e = \sqrt{\frac{2NL}{pr_c}} \qquad (5.5)$$

Due to the assumptions of having constant purchase cost, Q_e can also be calculated by finding the intersection of the ordering and carrying cost and solving for Q.

5.4.2   *Economic order interval*

In a situation of constant demand rate (one of the assumption of the EOQ model), an economic order quantity will be ordered at a constant period-icity. The constant time interval between orders plays an important role, even in a situation where some of hypotheses are not respected. It can be used as an indicator which provides a rough estimation as well as a basis for sophisticated strategies when demand becomes less simplistic, which will be further developed later in this chapter. This time interval, Economic Order Interval or Economic Time between Orders, T_e, can be obtained by dividing the EOQ by the average demand rate, D, of the considered period.

$$T_e = \frac{Q_e}{D} \qquad (5.6)$$

The role of the Economic Order Interval is illustrated in Fig. 5.4 which represents the evolution of the stock level is as a function of time for a case of constant demand rate.

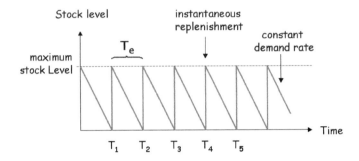

Fig. 5.4   Economic order interval and the evolution of the stock level.

5.4.3   *Sensitivity and economic order zone*

An important aspect in using the EOQ model is that, in practice, the parameters are usually whole units or simple fractions. For instance, the value of Q is usually a whole number since most products cannot be ordered in fractions. Time intervals between orders must also be rounded off to a planning period such as a week or day. Consequently, this practice influences the computed solution, while engendering a certain range of delta distance from a mathematically found optimal solution. To see the effect of these variations, it is possible to conduct sensitivity analyses so as to determine an appropriate level of accuracy. Let parameter ΔC be the acceptable cost deviation from the minimal cost $C(Q_e)$ related to the exact value of Q_e:

$$\Delta C = C(Q) - C(Q_e) \tag{5.7}$$

In operating practice, it is possible to define an acceptable ratio, i.e. a relative cost deviation $\frac{\Delta C}{C(Q_e)}$. For example, if a deviation of 8% from the minimal cost might be acceptable, the value of ΔC can be obtained accordingly. The issue then consists of determining what is the order quantity deviation ΔQ from Q_e that corresponds to the relative cost deviation $\frac{\Delta C}{C(Q_e)}$. For this purpose, the first step consists of developing the cost function around the optimum solution $Q = Q_e$.

$$C(Q) = Np + \frac{Q}{2}pr_c + \frac{N}{Q}L \qquad (5.8)$$

$$C(Q_e) = Np + \frac{Q_e}{2}pr_c + \frac{N}{Q_e}L \qquad (5.9)$$

$$C(Q) = C(Q_e) + \Delta Q C'(Q_e) + \frac{\Delta Q^2}{2}C''(Q_e) \qquad (5.10)$$

$$C(Q) = C(Q_e) + \frac{\Delta Q^2}{2}C''(Q_e) = C(Q_e) + \frac{NL}{Q_e{}^3}\Delta Q^2 \qquad (5.11)$$

$$\Delta C = C(Q) - C(Q_e) = \frac{NL}{Q_e{}^3}\Delta Q^2 = \frac{NL}{Q_e}\left(\frac{\Delta Q}{Q_e}\right)^2 \qquad (5.12)$$

$$\Delta Q = \pm\sqrt{\left(\frac{\Delta C}{C(Q_e)}\right)\left(\frac{C(Q_e)Q_e{}^3}{NL}\right)} = \pm\sqrt{\frac{\Delta C Q_e{}^3}{NL}} \qquad (5.13)$$

The final result shows that the order quantity deviation ΔQ is proportional to the square root of the cost deviation. Otherwise inversely, the relative cost deviation $\frac{\Delta C}{C(Q_e)}$ is proportional to the square of the order quantity deviation according to the relation:

$$\frac{\Delta C}{C(Q_e)} = \frac{NL}{C(Q_e)Q_e}\left(\frac{\Delta Q}{Q_e}\right)^2 \qquad (5.14)$$

The acceptable range of order quantity $Q_e - \Delta Q$ to $Q_e + \Delta Q$ is called the Economic Order Zone (EOZ). The practical consequence of this is that the optimal order quantity Q_e can be rounded up to any useful value as long as it is within the EOZ.

5.5 Inventory management methods

The purpose of inventory management methods is to determine the order quantity and time of replenishment. Depending on the chosen method and parameters (the order quantity and replenishment moment), the average quantity in stock will be directly influenced. The possible composition of the parameters takes one of the following forms:

(1) Fixed period and fixed quantity;
(2) Fixed period and variable quantity;
(3) Variable period and fixed quantity;
(4) Variable period and variable quantity.

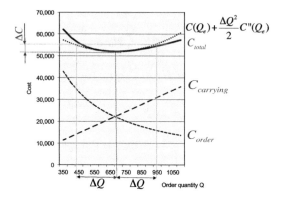

Fig. 5.5   Dependence of the cost components on the order quantity.

According to the variability of both parameters, inventory management methods can be categorised into four main categories, as illustrated in Table 5.2.

Table 5.2   Category of inventory management methods.

	Fixed period	Variable period
Fixed quantity	Fixed reordering	Reorder point, or (R, Q)-policy (s, S)-policy (continuous review)
Variable quantity	Replenishment or (S)-policy Periodic Order Quantity (POQ) (s, S)-policy (periodic review)	Part Period Balancing (PPB) Mc Laren's Order Moment (MOM)

Another classification of inventory management consists of differentiating review moment: periodic review versus continuous review methods. In a periodic review method, a replenishment decision is made periodically at specific times (for example, every week, at the end of month, and on on). In a continuous review method, the stock level is continuously checked and a replenishment decision can occur at any time. Variable period methods can belong to both categories (periodic or continuous review) depending on how they are applied, whether a decision is made at fixed time intervals (for example at the beginning of each planning period) or continuously. In the description of each method, the following symbols and definitions will be commonly referred to.

- On-hand inventory (S): Amount of items physically available in stock;
- Supply line (SL): Amount of items ordered but not yet delivered from suppliers;
- Back-order (BO): Amount of items that should have been shipped to customers at an earlier date;
- Inventory position (IP): Result of computation from $[S + SL - BO]$.

Each method will be applied to a fictive example which exhibits the following situation.

- Example item: ball bearing
- Unit price per piece: 1.20 EUR
- Inventory carrying cost rate per year: 15%/year
- Ordering cost (L): 100 EUR
- No safety stock: $S_s = 0$

5.5.1 *Fixed reordering method*

The fixed reordering method consists of ordering fixed quantity of items at a fixed time interval. In the inventory management of real-world situations, the application of this method is restricted to a few cases, which have almost constant demand and deal with low cost items. Unfortunately, in most of the real world cases, the demand is not constant which limits the boundary of application of this simplistic model.

Procedure of the fixed reordering method

The procedure concerns the computation of two main parameters:

- Compute the economic order quantity Q_e;
- Compute the economic order interval T_e;
- Apply both values to defining the next order moment of the quantity Q_e.

The typical evolution of the stock level is illustrated in Fig. 5.6. The solid line of the graph represents the theoretical behaviour of the stock, assuming a constant demand.

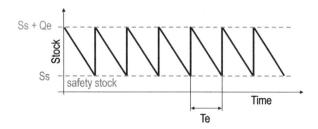

Fig. 5.6   Fixed reordering method.

Example application of fixed reordering method

The method is applied to the above-mentioned illustrative example. The key values are computed as $Q_e = 3350$ and $T_e = 4$ months, which gives the results in Table 5.3. The delivery of the first period is set to Q_e by default. The other data for the demand, the deliveries, and for the stock replenishment are presented in Table 5.4.

Summary of inventory performance with the fixed reordering method

- Average stock: 1538
- Inventory carrying cost: 277 EUR
- Total ordering cost: 300 EUR
- Total back-order: 500 $(pcs./year)$
- Total cost (without including back-order as cost): 577 EUR

5.5.2   *Replenishment method, S-policy*

When the demand is not constant and a fixed interval is still preferred, it is better to place orders while varying the order quantity. This method is suitable for applying to such a situation. The quantity should be calculated using the EOQ model so as to fill (replenish) the beginning stock level (of the concerned period). This method is called the replenishment method, having several other names such as the *Base stock policy*, the *Order-up-to policy*, or the *S-policy*.

Procedure of the replenishment method

The procedure of the replenishment method is given below:

- Compute the economic order quantity Q_e;
- Compute the economic order interval T_e;
- Identify, or compute, the safety stock S_s (later in this chapter, we will discuss how to compute an optimal level of safety stock which satisfies a firms' strategy);
- At each time of replenishment (the interval of T_e), compute the order quantity $Q_t = Q_e + S_s - S_t$, where S_t is the actual stock level (before delivery) at the time period of replenishment t, which is equivalent to the stock end of the $t-1$ time period.

The typical evolution of stock level is illustrated in Fig. 5.7.

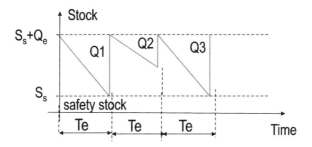

Fig. 5.7   Replenishment method.

Example application of the replenishment method

Assuming the same values for $Q_e = 3350$ and $T_e = 4$ months, Table 5.4 demonstrates result of applying this method.

Summary of inventory performance with the replenishment

- Average stock: 1654
- Inventory carrying cost: 298 *EUR*
- Total ordering cost: 300 *EUR*
- Total back-order: 500 *(pcs./year)*
- Total cost (without including back-order as cost): 598 *EUR*

Table 5.3 Fixed reordering method.

Month	1	2	3	4	5	6	7	8	9	10	11	12
Demand	800	900	950	1050	1200	400	400	1000	900	950	950	700
Delivery	3350				3350				3350			
Stock begin	3350	2550	1650	700	3000	1800	1400	1000	3350	2450	1500	550
Stock end	2550	1650	700	−350	1800	1400	1000	0	2450	1500	550	−150

Table 5.4 Replenishment method.

Month	1	2	3	4	5	6	7	8	9	10	11	12
Demand	800	900	950	1050	1200	400	400	1000	900	950	950	700
Delivery	3350				3700				3000			
Stock begin	3350	2550	1650	700	3350	2150	1750	1350	3350	2450	1500	550
Stock end	2550	1650	700	−350	2150	1750	1350	350	2450	1500	550	−150

The advantages and disadvantages of the replenishment method is summarised below.

Advantages

(a) The method requires little prior information;
(b) The order lot size is already defined;
(c) Thanks to its regularity of the replenishment interval, easy to integrate in a work schedule;
(d) It does not require constant monitoring, therefore requires low management costs.

Disadvantages

(a) It works better with a hypothesis of fairly constant demand with little variation;
(b) The stocking cost might be high since it tends to maintain a relatively high level of inventory if firms try to avoid stock-out;
(c) It does not take into account anticipated demand.

5.5.3 *Periodic order quantity*

When the demand is not constant but predictable, with the help of forecasting for instance, the Periodic Order Quantity (POQ) method is suitable. The POQ places orders, at fixed interval, of the quantity including the safety stock as well as the demand during the forthcoming interval.

Procedure of the periodic order quantity

The procedure of the POQ is presented below:

- Compute the economic order quantity Q_e;
- Compute the economic order interval T_e;
- Identify, or compute, the safety stock S_s (later, we will discuss how to compute a relevant safety stock level);
- At each time of replenishment (i at the interval of T_e period), compute D_{i+1} which is the average demand rate during the cycle of upcoming T_e periods. Then, compute the order quantity $Q_t = \bar{D}_{i+1}T_e + S_s - S_t$. For the sake of simplicity, $\bar{D}_{i+1}T_e$ can be replaced by the sum of demands

during the next T_e periods in case the demand rate of each period is known.

The typical evolution of the stock level is presented in Fig. 5.8.

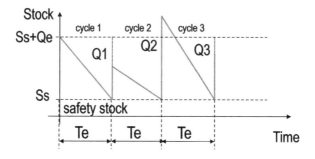

Fig. 5.8   Periodic order quantity.

Example application of the periodic order quantity

Based on the same values for $Q_e = 3350$ and $T_e = 4$ months, Table 5.5 demonstrates result of applying this method to the same demand data. The required delivery computation starts at month 1.

Summary of inventory performance with the periodic order quantity

- Average stock: 1683
- Inventory carrying cost: 303 *EUR*
- Total ordering cost: 300 *EUR*
- Total back-order: 0 (*pcs./year*)
- Total cost (without including back-order as cost): 603 *EUR*

In general, the POQ method contributes to reducing inventory carrying cost as well as back-orders by allowing lot sizes to vary. The following list compares the advantages and disadvantages of POQ.

Advantages

(a) The method works with little prior information;
(b) It requires very simple decision on order lot size;

(c) It is easy to integrate into a work schedule thanks to the regular interval of checking inventory;

(d) It is possible to integrate production schedule information.

Disadvantages

(a) The method requires a good knowledge of the forthcoming demand;

(b) It requires regular checks of order quantity based on future demand, therefore more costly to manage.

5.5.4 *Reorder point, (R, Q)-policy*

The two previous methods adapt to a non-constant demand by varying the order quantity while keeping the order periodicity constant. The Reorder Point method works in an opposite way. It keeps the order quantity constant but varies the order periodicity, i.e. the time interval between two successive orders. Accordingly, the Reorder Point method places an order of quantity $Q = Q_e$ when the stock is equal or inferior to a critical level called reorder point, S_c. R in the name (R,Q) here means the *Reorder* point value. This reorder point must take into account the delay between order placement and the delivery lead-time of items. This time interval is called the replenishment time, R. This policy can be used with a periodic or a continuous review process The average demand rate should be known in order to compute the reorder point. However, periodic demand forecasting is not mandatory.

Procedure of the reorder point method

The procedure of the reorder point is presented below:

- Determine the economic order quantity Q_e;
- Identify or determine the replenishment time R;
- Identify, or compute, the safety stock S_s;
- Calculate the reorder point $S_c = S_s + \mathcal{R}\bar{D}$, where $\bar{D}$ is the average demand rate during the replenishment time;
- Place delivery order of Q_e if the stock level equals or is inferior to the reorder point. It is a typical case of periodic review during which the algorithm checks whether the actual level of stock end *crosses* the reorder point line.

The typical evolution of the stock level in the case of continuous review are presented in Fig. 5.9.

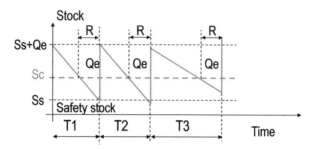

Fig. 5.9   Fixed reordering method.

Example application of reorder point

Assuming the same values for $Q_e = 3350$ and $T_e = 4$ months, and the known replenishment time $\mathcal{R} = 1$ month, Table 5.5 demonstrates the result of applying this method to the same demand data. The required delivery computation starts at month 1. First of all, the S_c should be computed by the following formula:

$$\bar{D} = 850, \; S_c = \mathcal{R} \times \bar{D} = 1 \times 850 = 850$$

Summary of inventory performance with the reorder point method

- Average stock: 2075
- Inventory carrying cost: $374\,EUR$
- Total ordering cost: $400\,EUR$ (based on the number of effective deliveries)
- Total back-order: 0
- Total cost (without including back-order as cost): $774\,EUR$

In the above example, the on-hand stock S, which is the stock end value, crosses occasionally the reorder point S_c following the stock consumptions and deliveries, such as on periods 3, 8, and 11 which are then identified as

Table 5.5   Periodic order quantity.

Month	1	2	3	4	5	6	7	8	9	10	11	12
Demand	800	900	950	1050	1200	400	400	1000	900	950	950	700
Delivery	3700			3000				3500				
Stock begin	3700	2900	2000	1050	3000	1800	1400	1000	3500	2600	1650	700
Stock end	2900	2000	1050	0	1800	1400	1000	0	2600	1650	700	0

Table 5.6   Reorder point.

Month	1	2	3	4	5	6	7	8	9	10	11	12
Demand	800	900	950	1050	1200	400	400	1000	900	950	950	700
Delivery	3350			3350				3350				3350
Stock begin	3350	2550	1650	4050	3000	1800	1400	1000	3350	2450	1500	3900
Stock end	2550	1650	700	3000	1800	1400	1000	0	2450	1500	550	3200
Order			3350				3350				3350	

the reorder moment. The example shows a typical case when the replenishment time $\mathcal{R}$ is shorter than the ideal replenishment cycle T which is computed from the economic order interval. However, the situation $\mathcal{R} > T$ can easily happen in practice. That means the supply lead-time is longer than the expected economic order interval.

In such a situation if the same method is applied to, before receiving the ordered quantity Q_e, the next order period reaches, and the stock level is always lower than the reorder point. Subsequently, the decision cannot happen as expected since the on-hand inventory S never crosses the reorder point S_c. The situation is illustrated on the left side in Fig. 5.10.

There are different ways to solve this problem. One simple method suggests to multiply the period by an integer number as if orders are placed to cover several order periods. This leads to using a fictive stock defined as $S_f = S + n \times Q_e$, where n represents how many order cycles T are included in one cycle of replenishment $\mathcal{R}$. The value n can be computed by the following formula:

$$n = Trunc\left(\frac{\mathcal{R}\bar{D}}{Q_e}\right)$$

where $Trunc(x)$ is a function to truncate the number x to an integer by removing the fractional part of x.

The right side of Fig. 5.10 illustrates the use of a fictive stock with $n = 1$.

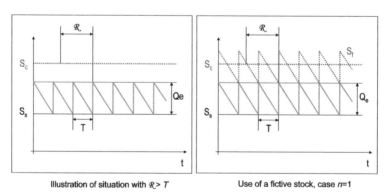

Illustration of situation with $\mathcal{R} > T$ Use of a fictive stock, case $n=1$

Fig. 5.10   Reorder point method — stock evolution.

Another practical way to solve the problem consists of using the inventory position, IP, instead of the on-hand inventory, S, to control the replenishment decision. Therefore an order of fixed quantity, Q_e, is placed at every time when IP reaches (case of continuous review) or crosses (case of periodic review) the reorder point. Figure 5.11 illustrates the reorder point with IP in case of periodic review.

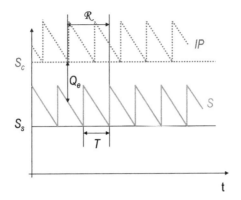

Fig. 5.11   Reordering method — using inventory position IP, case $n = 1$.

The advantages and disadvantages of the RP method are discussed below.

Advantages

(a) The method can be applied with little prior information;
(b) It is relatively simple to decide the order lot size;
(c) It takes the production schedule into account;
(d) It can be applied without a computer.

Disadvantages

(a) If the demand is constant, it gives satisfactory results;
(b) It does require constant monitoring of the stock level;
(c) The result tends to maintain high level of inventory.

5.5.5   *The (s, S)-policy*

Among several management models of single item inventory systems, it is well known that an optimal policy exists within the class of (s, S)-policies. With (s, S)-policy, an order is placed to increase the item's inventory position to the level S as soon as this inventory position reaches or drops below the level s. The (s, S)-policy is similar to the Reorder point, (R, Q)-*Policy*, except that the inventory position IP is refilled up to a predefined level S. In case of a periodic review process, the (s, S)- and (R, Q)-polices differ by the replenishment quantity Q ordered; $Q = S - s$ for the (s, S)-policy, while $Q = Q_e$ for the (R, Q)-policy. In case of a continuous review process, the two policies are identical since $s = $ *Reorder point* (S_c) and $S - s = Q_e$.

The evolution of stock level in case of continuous review is presented in Fig. 5.12.

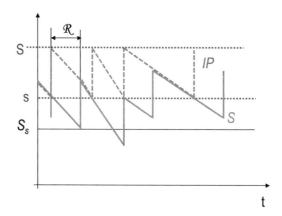

Fig. 5.12 (s, S)-policy with continuous review.

If a periodic review process is used, a replenishment order is launched only if $IP \leq s$. If the demand rate decreases significantly, this can lead to periods with no replenishment, as illustrated in Fig. 5.13. In some literature, the (s, S)-policy with periodic review is also called an (R,S)-policy.

5.5.6   *Part period balancing*

The Part Period Balancing (PPB) method allows both the order quantity and periodicity to vary. The method is looking to minimise the total cost by balancing the cost of carrying inventory with the ordering cost. In determining the ordering lot-size, PPB tries to equate the total costs of placing orders and carrying inventory by empirically searching for an alternative lot-size choice at the beginning of period t.

For instance, if the period of decision making is $t = 1$, the potential alternatives to examine can be summarised as the following cases:

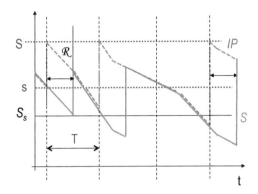

Fig. 5.13   (s, S)-policy with periodic review.

(i) ordering the amount of period 1 only,
(ii) ordering the amount which covers period 1 and 2,
(iii) ordering the amount which covers period 1, 2, and 3.

Subsequently, a specific algorithm is required to find the ordering moment at which the inventory carrying cost for the alternative which most accurately approximates the computed ordering cost. The resulting lot-size is equivalent to the sum of the requirement during the period until the next ordering moment.

There are several ways of implementing the PPB principal. The following procedure illustrates the PPB method applied to the same demand data listed below:

p = item price or value
r_c = inventory carrying cost rate per planning period
D_n = demand for planning period n
$C_{s(n)}$ = stocking cost for during the next planning periods n
L = ordering cost
Q = order quantity, i.e. dynamic lot-size

Given that the annual inventory carrying cost rate $= 0.15$, the monthly inventory carrying cost rate is computed as $= 0.0125$. A cost factor, c_f, which represents the cost of carrying one item in inventory during a period of time, can be computed as $c_f = 0.0125 \times 1.2(EUR) = 0.015(EUR)$.

Let us consider the alternative lot-size choices available at the beginning of period 1. The lot-size alternative becomes the quantity of delivery at period 1 which will cover the demand until the end of considered period. The calculation is based on the average inventory carrying rate per month and average inventory level during the concerned periods. Then compare the computed stocking cost with the ordering cost.

(i) period 1 only: $c_f \times \frac{800}{2} = 0.015 \times 400 = 6$

(ii) period 1 and 2: $0.015 \times \left[900 + \frac{800}{2} + \frac{900}{2}\right] = 0.015 \times 1750 = 26.25$

(iii) period 1, 2, and 3:
$0.015 \times \left[950 + 900 + \frac{800}{2} + 950 + \frac{900}{2} + \frac{950}{2}\right] = 0.015 \times 4125 = 61.875$

(iv) period 1 to 4:
$0.015 \times \left[1050 + 950 + 900 + \frac{800}{2} + 1050 + 950 + \frac{900}{2} + 1050 + \frac{950}{2} + \frac{1050}{2}\right]$
$= 0.015 \times 7795 = 116.925$

The option (ii) of *period 1 and 2* means what will be the inventory carrying cost if the ordering lot-size is chosen for covering the requirements for period 1 and 2. For each line of computation, the following formula is used:

inventory carry cost of a certain periods $= c_f \times$ average inventory level

Now, comparing the ordering cost, 100 with the computed inventory carrying cost for each alternative, we can select two potential options: (i) coverage of period 1 to 3, and (ii) coverage of periods 1 to 4. Since the nearest value to 100 is 117, we can conclude that the order lot-size at period 1 shall cover the total amount of period 1 to 4, which gives $Q_4 = 800 + 900 + 950 + 1050 = 3700$. Finally, this value is put as the amount of *delivery at period* 1. After the delivery of period 1 is defined, the method continues starting from period 5 in order to define the delivery amount of period 5. By comparing the options between stock cost for period 5 to

- period 5 to 8: stock cost $= 85.5$
- period 5 to 9: stock cost $= 146.3$

As 85.5 is the nearest value of 100, the order lot-size for covering the demand from period 5 to period 8 is chosen. For the purpose of computing stocking cost used in the procedure, the following short-cut formula can be applicable.

$$C_{s(n)} = \frac{p \times r_c}{2} \sum_{n=1}^{i} (2n - 1) D_{t^0 + n}$$

where, n is the distance index from the based period t^0 from which the procedure starts.

$$Q = \sum_{n=1}^{i} D_{t^0+n}$$

where t is the identified period (t^1) that next ordering lot should cover from t^0.

The corresponding data for the demand, the orders and for the evolution of the stock level are presented in Table 5.7. During low demand periods, the method yields a smaller lot-size and longer interval between orders than high demand periods.

Summary of inventory performance with the PPB method

- Average stock: 1683
- Inventory carrying cost: 303 *EUR*
- Total ordering cost: 300 *EUR*
- Total back-order: 0 *(pcs./year)*
- Total cost (without including back-order as cost): 603 *EUR*

The advantages and disadvantages of the PPB method are discussed below.

Advantages

(a) The method integrates production schedule information;
(b) The method tries to constantly optimise inventory and order lot size;
(c) It works well even with irregular demand.

Disadvantages

(a) This method requires precise demand data;
(b) The level of complexity for making decision on ordering moment and lot-size is relatively high;
(c) It requires constant check and feedback for the purpose of comparing nearest value between two options;
(d) For the purpose of implementing the method, computer or a similar tool is necessary.

Manufacturing Operations Management

Table 5.7 Part period balancing.

Month	1	2	3	4	5	6	7	8	9	10	11	12
Demand	800	900	950	1050	1200	400	400	1000	900	950	950	700
Delivery	3700				3000				3500			
Stock begin	3700	2900	2000	1050	3000	1800	1400	1000	3500	2600	1650	700
Stock end	2900	2000	1050	0	1800	1400	1000	0	2600	1650	700	0
$C_s(n)$	6	26.25	61.875	117	9	18	33	85.5	6.75	13.88	36.25	61.5
Lot decision	no	no	no	yes	no	no	no	yes	no	no	no	no
Lot size Q				3700				3000				(3500)

5.5.7 *Mc Laren's order moment*

Similar to the PPB method, the Mc Laren's Order Moment (MOM) allows both the order quantity and periodicity to vary. The MOM heuristics tries to combine the advantages of economic order quantity with the part period criteria.

In the MOM method, the order quantity is determined by a search for equality between the inventory carrying cost of the actual case with that of an ideal case characterised by a constant demand of identical cumulated volume over the considered horizon. Contrarily to the PPB method, the MOM method does not take into account the inventory carrying cost concerning the demand quantity of the current planning period.

The algorithm of the MOM method is presented below, and the result of application is presented in Table 5.8:

(1) Compute the economy order quantity Q_e;
(2) Compute the economic order interval T_e;
(3) Compute the cumulated reference moment MOM_r;

$$MOM_r = \bar{D}_p \left[\sum_{t=0}^{T^*-1} t + T^* \left(T_e - T^*\right) \right]$$

with $T^* =$ largest integer $\leq T_e$
(4) Compute the cumulated effective moment MOM_t;

$$MOM_t = \sum_{n=1}^{t} (n-1) D_n$$

(5) If $MOM_t \geq MOM_r$, determine the number of periods t^o to be used for computing the order quantity by running the following decision test on the last period of consideration k;

$$\text{if } C_s D_k (k-1) \leq L \text{ then } t^o = k$$

$$\text{if } C_s D_k (k-1) > L \text{ then } t^o = k - 1$$

with $C_s =$ inventory carrying cost of one part period
(6) Compute the order quantity $Q = \sum_{n=0}^{t^o} D_n$;

Table 5.8 Mc Laren's order moment.

Month	1	2	3	4	5	6	7	8	9	10	11	12
Demand	800	900	950	1050	1200	400	400	1000	900	950	950	700
Delivery	3700				3900					3500		
Stock begin	3700	2900	2000	1050	3900	2700	2300	1900	900	3500	2550	1600
Stock end	2900	2000	1050	0	2700	2300	1900	900	0	2550	1600	900
MOM_t	0	900	2800	5950	0	400	1200	4200	7800	0	950	2350
$MOM_t > MOM_r$?	no	no	no	yes	no	no	no	no	yes	no	no	no
$C_s D_k(k-1)$				47.25					54			
$C_s D_k(k-1) > L$				no					5			
$t^0=$				4					5			
Q	3700			3700	3900				3900			

Summary of inventory performance with the MOM method

- Average stock: 1992
- Inventory carrying cost: 359 *EUR*
- Total ordering cost: 300 *EUR*
- Total back-order: 0
- Total cost (without including back-order as cost): 659 *EUR*

Advantages

(a) The method integrates production schedule information;
(b) It can constantly optimise inventory and order lot size;
(c) It works with irregular demand.

Disadvantages

(a) The method requires precise demand data;
(b) The degree of complexity of decision, for both an order placement and lot size, is very high;
(c) It requires constant check and feedback;
(d) The implementation of the algorithm requires computation equipment.

5.5.8 *Summary of inventory management methods*

- There is a trade-off between inventory carrying costs and ordering costs.
- The various inventory management methods, which have been presented so far, focus on optimising this trade off.
- In practice, if the chosen order quantity Q varies slightly from the theoretical Qe, there will only be a slight effect on total costs.
- In an EOQ model, a 100% error in order quantity results in a 25% error in the total costs.

When considering the relative performance of the various inventory management methods, the degree of variability and uncertainty of the demand and other parameters must be taken into account. Some simulation studies have shown that, when the uncertainty degree and the number of levels in the bill of material increase, the difference in the performance of the various methods tends to vanish.

5.6   Managing uncertainty

Uncertainty is an important factor in operations management. Understanding how uncertainty influences production and inventory management greatly influences operating performance. If it is not managed relevantly, the stock levels can uselessly rise too high or fall too low. This section is dedicated to introducing basic categories of uncertainty and how to manage the safety stock in order to mitigate the negative impact of uncertainty on the inventory performance. The following subsection fist introduces the different sources of uncertainty.

5.6.1   *Sources of uncertainty*

Table 5.9 and Table 5.10 illustrate the sources of uncertainties which may be introduced unexpectedly during operations, which then can influence the supply or the demand in terms of the lead-time or quantity.

Table 5.9   Example sources of uncertainty — supply side.

	Supply
Lead-times	Modification of the supply lead-time Variation of transport time Unexpected events such as strikes, natural disaster Difficulty in raw material supply
Quantity	Modification of the delivered quantity Problem with raw material supply Unexpected production rejection Machine break-downs Employee's absence

5.6.2   *Safety stock and lead time*

Earlier in this chapter, it was mentioned that inventory can be seen as a form of stored capacity that can help a firm retain its service level (delivery delay and reliability) if production capacities alone are not sufficient to satisfy customer's orders. Safety stock plays the same role; it helps protect a firm against different forms of uncertainty. Safety stock can be seen as a buffer that is added to the stock resulting from the real demand and the inventory management rules.

Table 5.10   Example sources of uncertainty — demand side.

	Demand
Lead-times	Modification of the demand due date Order anticipated or delayed Delta between forecasted and ordered amounts Planning modification of a parent item Rejected production of a parent item
Quantity	Modification of the ordered quantity Order quantity increased/decreased Delta between forecasted and ordered amount Modification of a parent item requirement Rejected production of a parent item

The same logic can be applied to lead-times. If there are uncertainties in the lead-times of certain operations, the risk related to these uncertainties can be reduced by adding a safety lead-time to the real lead-time. Obviously, safety stock and safety lead-time do have certain drawbacks and costs such as:

(i) Higher storage cost;
(ii) Higher obsolescence risk;
(iii) Introduction of virtual demand to the planning system;
(iv) Disconnection from actual needs of the clients.

Both safety stock and lead-time can be applied independently of the source of uncertainty. However, it is interesting to compare their effectiveness with respect to the sources of uncertainty. Some simulation studies have shown that time related uncertainties tend to be more efficiently covered by a safety lead-time, whereas quantity related uncertainties seems to be more efficiently covered by safety stock. Often, uncertainties on the supply side are more related to time than quantity. Similarly, uncertainties on the demand side are more often related to quantity than time. Subsequently, using safety lead-time would be recommended on the supply side and using safety stock in the demand side.

5.6.3   *Performance criteria of inventory management*

The size of the safety stock depends on the delivery performances that the firm wants to offer to its customers, as well as on the cost it is ready to pay for reaching this targeted performance level. Therefore, the definition and the choice of performance criteria are of importance. Various types of performance criteria may be chosen, depending on the business strategy of a firm. For instance, firms competing on price tend to focus on cost criteria while others, competing on service, might focus on the ratio of satisfied orders. The next section will discuss the following three common performance criteria:

- Probability of shortage;
- Order satisfaction level;
- Total cost.

5.6.4   *Performance criterion 1: Stock-out probability*

The stock-out probability corresponds to the risk of running out of stock during a replenishment cycle. Estimating this probability requires data on the probability of obtaining various demand levels. Once these are known, a firm can use safety stock or safety lead-time to reach a target stock-out probability which can be considered as the performance criterion. As seen before, this does imply additional costs. The key issue is to determine how much inventory carrying cost to accept in order to reach the target level. The following example illustrates how to compute it.

If $p(D)$ is the probability of the demand during the replenishment time, D, then the stock out probability p_r is given by:

$$p_r = \sum_{D > S_c} p(D)$$

where:

S_c: reorder point
D: demand during the replenishment time

The demand during the replenishment time of the finished product inventory of MISA, a company selling coffee machines, is given in Fig. 5.14 for the next planning horizon.

Let us assume that the reorder point used by MISA to trigger replenishment is 150 units. Then the probability of shortage of this product can be computed as below:

$$p_r = \sum_{D > S_c} p(D) = p(D = 170) + p(D = 190) = 17\% + 3\% = 20\%$$

If the demand during the replenishment time can be described by a continuous distribution $f(D)$, then the stock out probability can be calculated

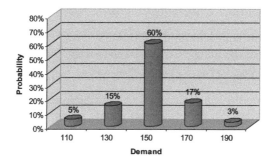

Fig. 5.14 Demand probability during the replenishment time — Discrete distribution.

using:

$$p_r = \int_{D>S_c} f(D)\,\mathrm{d}D$$

This situation is illustrated in Fig. 5.15.

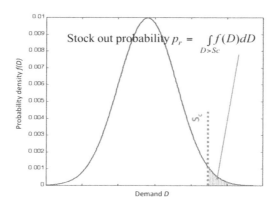

Fig. 5.15 Demand probability during the replenishment time — Continuous distribution.

Considering the previous expression for p_r, it is obvious that improving customer service (i.e. reducing stock-out probability) will require increasing the reorder point S_c, which consequently introduces extra costs for additional inventory. This is a strategic decision, which is difficult to evaluate since there are many non-quantitative advantages of guaranteeing high customer service.

5.6.5 *Performance criterion 2: Order satisfaction level*

Order satisfaction is a delivery performance index defined as the ratio of the on time delivered quantity over the requested one. Its value p_c can be calculated according to the following relation:

$$p_c = \frac{\text{delivered quant.}}{\text{required quant.}} = \frac{\text{available quant.}}{\text{available quant.} + \text{non available quant.}}$$

$$\cong 1 - \frac{\text{non available quant.}}{\text{available quant.}}$$

If the demand can be described by a discrete distribution, p_c can be calculated on the basis of the following relations:

- Available quantity during one replenishment cycle: the order quantity Q
- Non-available quantity during one replenishment cycle: $\sum_{D=S_c+1}^{D_{max}} P_D (D - S_c)$

where:

S_c: reorder point
D: demand during the replenishment time
P_D: probability of having demand amount of D during the replenishment time

$$p_c = 1 - \frac{1}{Q} \sum_{D=S_c+1}^{D_{max}} P_D (D - S_c)$$

Considering again the previous MISA example and knowing that:

$Q = 500$ pcs.
$S_c = 150$ pcs.
$S_s = 100$ pcs.

The difference $(D - S_c)$ between the demand D and the maximum deliverable quantity S_c during the replenishment cycle is illustrated on Fig. 5.16.

The resulting non-available quantity $\sum_{D=S_c+1}^{D_{max}} P_D (D - S_c)$ is shown in Fig. 5.17.

The situation is summarised in Table 5.11.

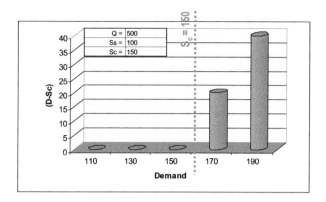

Fig. 5.16 Demand difference $(D - S_c)$ during the replenishment time.

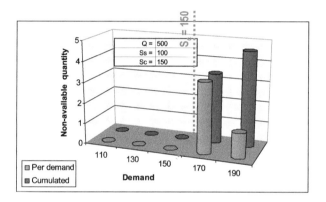

Fig. 5.17 Non-available quantity during the replenishment time—Discrete distribution.

The order satisfaction level is calculated according to:

$$p_c = 1 - \frac{1}{500} [0.17 \times 20 + 0.03 \times 40] = 1 - \frac{1}{500} \times 4.6 = 0.9908$$

Suppose now that MISA wants to reduce its inventory costs and therefore decides to reduce the safety stock from 100 to 50 pcs. The reorder point will consequently become $150 - 50 = 100$. This leads to the new non available quantity illustrated in Fig. 5.18 and the new order satisfaction level is given in Table 5.12.

The order satisfaction level is then calculated according to:

$$P_c = 1 - \frac{1}{500} \times 49.6 = 0.9008$$

Table 5.11 Order satisfaction level calculation.

Demand (D)	Probability (p_D)	($D - S_c$)	Non-available quantity $p_D(D - S_c)$	Order satisfaction level
110	5%	–	–	–
130	15%	–	–	–
150	60%	–	–	–
170	17%	20	3.4	–
190	3%	40	1.2	–
	100%	–	4.6	99.1%

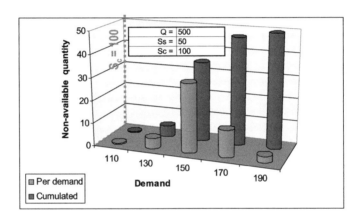

Fig. 5.18 Non-available quantity during the replenishment time.

The reduction of the safety stock by 50 units leads to a drastic decrease in the order satisfaction level, i.e. from 99% to 90%.

If the demand during the replenishment time can be described by a continuous distribution $f(D)$, then the non available quantity can be calculated by the following relation:

$$\text{non-available quantity} = \int_{D>S_c}^{\infty} (D - S_c)\, f(D)\, dD$$

And the order satisfaction level p_c is then:

$$p_c = 1 - \frac{1}{Q} \int_{D>S_c}^{\infty} (D - S_c) f(D) dD$$

Table 5.12   Order satisfaction level calculation with non-available quantity.

Demand (D)	Probability (p_D)	$(D - S_c)$	Non available quantity $p_D(D - S_c)$	Order satisfaction level
110	5%	10	0.5	–
130	15%	30	4.5	–
150	60%	50	30	–
170	17%	70	11.9	–
190	3%	90	2.7	–
–	100%	–	49.6	90.1%

5.6.6   Performance criterion 3: Total cost

Depending on the availability of data on the probability of the demand during the replenishment time, and if the stock-out cost can be estimated, it is possible to evaluate the total cost. On this basis, an optimal solution (minimum total cost) can be looked for by adapting the order quantity Q and the reorder point (or safety stock). The total cost function is given by the following equation:

$$C_{total} = C_{carrying} + C_{order} + C_{stock\text{-}out} \qquad (5.15)$$

$$C_{total} = C_s \left[\frac{Q}{2} + S_s \right] + \frac{N}{Q}L + \frac{N}{Q}C_N \left[\sum_{D=S_c+1}^{D_{max}} p_D(D - S_c) \right] \qquad (5.16)$$

where:

C_N: cost of non-satisfaction per unit
C_{total}: total cost
C_S: unit inventory carrying cost per period
D: demand during the replenishment time
$\bar{D}_p$: average demand per period
L: ordering (or set-up) cost
N: demand during the considered planning horizon
p_D: probability of demand during the replenishment time
Q: order quantity
R: replenishment time (in period)
S_c: reorder point
S_s: safety stock

Total cost when using the reorder point method

When a reorder point method is used for inventory management, the reorder point S_c can be integrated into the previous Eq. (5.16) by replacing the safety stock S_s by $(S_c - \bar{D}_p R)$, as indicated below. The total cost can be optimised by solving for Q and S_c in the following equation:

$$C_{total} = C_s \left[\frac{Q}{2} + (S_c - \bar{D}_p R) \right] + \frac{N}{Q}L + \frac{N}{Q}C_N \left[\sum_{D=S_c+1}^{D_{max}} p_D(D - S_c) \right]$$

$$(5.17)$$

Table 5.13   Example demand data.

3500	4000	4500	5000	5500	6000	6500	7000	7500
2%	5%	10%	15%	20%	18%	15%	10%	5%

This optimisation is illustrated for a specific example characterised by the following demand data on Table 5.13 and parameters:

Value of one unit $p = 3$ EUR
Annual inventory carrying cost rate $C_y = 0.18$
Replenishment time $R = 10$ days
Ordering cost $L = 500$ EUR
Estimated cost of non-satisfaction $C_N = 0.3$ EUR
One year $= 220$ days
Average annual demand $N = 125400$ unit

The corresponding total cost evolution is given on Fig. 5.19.

5.7   Safety stock calculation

As discussed previously, uncertainty can affect the demand (variability of the demand per period), as well as the lead-times (variation of the replenishment time). These two sources of uncertainty have a cumulative effect that must be taken into account in calculating the most appropriate level of safety stock. For that purpose, both quantity and time variations are modelled by statistical distributions. These are described by appropriate probability density functions such as normal, gamma, exponential, triangular, and so forth. Fig. 5.20 and Fig. 5.21 provide illustrations of the

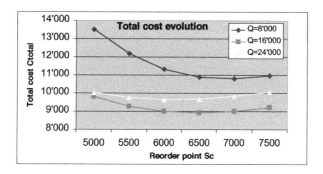

Fig. 5.19   Example of cost optimisation using the total cost criterion.

characteristics of the four example distributions.

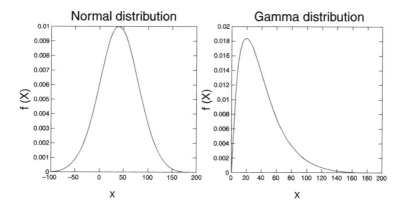

Fig. 5.20   Probability distribution functions — normal and gamma.

For the sake of simplicity, the approach presented in this section for calculating safety stock will be restricted to the uncertainties modelled by normal distributions. However, the procedure can also be applied to other distribution types. The normal distribution is characterised by the following probability density function $f(x)$:

$$f(x) = \frac{1}{\sqrt{2\pi\sigma^2}} e^{-\frac{(x-\mu)^2}{2\sigma^2}} \quad \forall x \in \mathcal{R} \tag{5.18}$$

where $\mu = \text{mean}, \sigma = \text{variance}$.

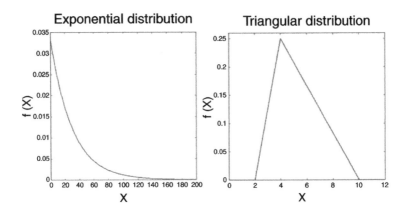

Fig. 5.21   Probability distribution functions — exponential and triangular.

5.7.1   *Merging different sources of uncertainty*

It is important to determine the cumulative effect resulting from combining different sources of uncertainty so that one single safety stock is capable of covering several sources of uncertainty.

Combination of normal distributions

The effect of combining several normal independent distributions is described below: Let $X_i(\mu_i, \sigma_i)$ be independent normal distributions of mean μ_l and variance σ_l^2. If a and b_i are real numbers, then the variable X is a normal distribution $X(\mu, \sigma)$ with:

$$X = a + b_1 X_1 + b_2 X_2 + \cdots + b_m X_m \tag{5.19}$$

$$\mu = a + \sum_{i=1}^{m} b_i \mu_i \tag{5.20}$$

$$\sigma^2 = \sum_{i=1}^{m} b_i^2 \sigma_i^2 \tag{5.21}$$

This means that the combination of several independent normal distributions leads to a normal distribution. The combined distribution shows several important characteristics for inventory management. In particular, it is interesting to look at the standard deviation σ and the coefficient of variation v of the combined distribution X.

$$\sigma = \sqrt{\sum_{i=1}^{m} b_i^2 \sigma_i^2} \tag{5.22}$$

$$v = \frac{\sigma}{\mu} = \frac{\sqrt{\sum_{i=1}^{m} b_i^2 \sigma_i^2}}{a + \sum_{i=1}^{m} b_i \mu_i} \tag{5.23}$$

This exemplifies the fact that the standard deviation σ of the combined distribution X is not the sum of the standard deviations of the single distributions σ_i but the square root of their sum.

Combination of normal distributions in inventory management

For the purpose of better understanding the consequences of the combination of normal distributions, three application cases will be illustrated:

(1) Application case 1: determining the monthly demand of a finished product on the basis of 4 weekly demand distributions.
(2) Application case 2: determining the aggregate weekly demand for a component belonging to the bill of material of four different finished products on the basis of the weekly finished product demand distributions.
(3) Application case 3: determining the weekly demand for a component required 4 times in the bill of material of one finished product on the basis of the weekly finished product demand distribution.

Application case 1

The four weekly demands $Xi(\mu_i, \sigma_i)$ with $i = 1$ to 4 are given in Table 5.14:

Table 5.14   Probability of demand during replenishment time R — Case 1.

	week 1	week 2	week 3	week 4
Demand mean	2550	2840	2760	2630
Demand standard deviation	536	540	414	658

The monthly demand distribution $X(\mu, \sigma)$ is a combination of the four independent weekly ones. The mean and standard deviation can thus be determined using the following relations:

$$\mu = \sum_{i=1}^{4} \mu_i = 2550 + 2840 + 2760 + 2630 = 10780 \qquad (5.24)$$

$$\sigma = \sqrt{\sum_{l=1}^{4} \sigma_l^2} = \sqrt{536^2 + 540^2 + 414^2 + 658^2} = 1088 \qquad (5.25)$$

It is interesting to compare the coefficient of variation of the four weekly demands with that of the monthly demand. The result is provided in Table 5.15. It is observed that the coefficient of variation of the monthly demand is much smaller than those of the four weekly demands. This effect is called *pooling effect*.

Table 5.15   Comparison of coefficient of variation.

	week 1	week 2	week 3	week 4	month
Demand mean	2550	2840	2760	2630	10780
Demand standard deviation	536	540	414	658	1088
Coefficient of variation	21%	19%	15%	25%	10%

Application case 2

In order to facilitate the comparison with case 1, the same statistical data will be used. They are given in Table 5.16.

Table 5.16   Probability of demand during replenishment time R — Case 2.

	week 1	week 2	week 3	week 4
Demand mean	2550	2840	2760	2630
Demand standard deviation	536	540	414	658

The weekly aggregate demand distribution $X(\mu, \sigma)$ is a combination of the four independent weekly ones. Its mean and standard deviation are

Table 5.17   Probability of demand during replenishment time R — Case 3.

	product
Demand mean	2695
Demand standard deviation	537

determined using the following relations:

$$\mu = \sum_{i=1}^{4} \mu_i = 2550 + 2840 + 2760 + 2630 = 10780 \qquad (5.26)$$

$$\sigma = \sqrt{\sum_{l=1}^{} 4\sigma_l{}^2} = \sqrt{536^2 + 540^2 + 414^2 + 658^2} = 1088 \qquad (5.27)$$

Thus the aggregate weekly demand distribution is the same as the monthly demand of case 1. The same pooling effect induces an important reduction of the coefficient of variation.

Application case 3

For this case, and to facilitate again the comparison with case 1 and 2, similar statistical data are used. They are given in Table 5.17.

The weekly component demand distribution $X(\mu, \sigma)$ is a multiple (by 4) of the weekly one. The mean and standard deviation are determined using the following relations:

$$\mu = 4\mu_l = 4 \times 2695 = 10780 \qquad (5.28)$$

$$\sigma = \sqrt{b_l{}^2 \sigma_l{}^2} = \sqrt{4^2 \times 537^2} = 4 \times 537 = 2148 \qquad (5.29)$$

The results, summarised in Table 5.18 are totally different from the previous ones. Although the mean is identical, the standard deviation is much higher because in this case there is no pooling effect. This is because this case does not involve the combination of independent distributions (uncertainty sources), but the multiplication by 4 of one single distribution. Consequently, the coefficient of variation remains unaffected.

5.7.2   *Variability of demand during the replenishment time*

As mentioned earlier, there are the two main sources of uncertainty, the variability of the demand D and the variability of the replenishment time

Table 5.18   Resulting coefficient of variation.

	product	component
Demand mean	2695	10780
Demand standard deviation	537	2148
Coefficient of variation	20%	20%

R. If other sources of uncertainty exist, they can be integrated using the same procedure. In practice, the usual available data are some statistical information about:

- The variability of the demand per planning period D_p;
- The variability of the replenishment time R.

It is generally possible to extract approximate value for describing the variability of D_p and R by the following normal probability distributions:

$$D_p(\bar{D}_p, \sigma_{D_p}) \tag{5.30}$$

$$R(\bar{R}, \sigma_R) \tag{5.31}$$

On this basis, the procedure for determining the safety stock consists of 4 steps:

(1) Calculating the variability of the demand D_R during the replenishment time due to the variability of D_p;
(2) Calculating the variability of the demand D_R during the replenishment time due to the variability of R;
(3) Calculating the variability of the demand D_R during the replenishment time resulting from the combination of the two previous variability sources;
(4) Determining the safety stock related to a specific performance criterion.

Step 1 — variability due to D_p

The computation of the variability of the demand during the replenishment time due to the variability of the demand per period D_p corresponds to application case 1 above. It requires the combination of R independent probability distributions. Thus the variability of the demand during the replenishment time due to the variability of D_p is:

$$D_R^D \left(\bar{R}\bar{D}_p, \sqrt{\bar{R}}\sigma_{D_p} \right)$$

Step 2 — variability due to R

The variability of the replenishment time R is a time distribution; it must be transformed into a quantity distribution. This consists of a change of variable or by multiplying the time distribution $R\left(\bar{R}, \sigma_R\right)$ by the mean demand per period $\bar{D}_p$. This is similar to the calculation shown in the application case 3 above. Thus the variability of the demand during the replenishment time due to the variability of R is:

$$D_R^R(\bar{D}_p\bar{R}, \bar{D}_p\sigma_R)$$

Of course the unit used must be coherent; i.e. R and σR must be expressed in planning periods.

Step 3 — variability due to the combination of the variability of R and D_p

The two previous sources of variability are then combined to give the final variability of the demand during the replenishment time D_R

$$D_R(\bar{R}\bar{D}_p; \sqrt{\bar{D}_p^2\sigma_R^2 + \bar{R}\sigma_{D_p}{}^2})$$

Thus, the variability of the demand during the replenishment time is characterised by:

mean: $\bar{D}_R = \bar{R}\bar{D}_p$

variance: $\sigma_{DR}{}^2 = \bar{D}_p^2\sigma_R^2 + \bar{R}\sigma_{D_p}{}^2$

standard deviation: $\sigma_{DR} = \sqrt{\bar{D}_p^2\sigma_R^2 + \bar{R}\sigma_{D_p}{}^2}$

5.7.3 *Safety stock calculation using the stock-out probability criterion*

With this approach, the safety stock is determined setting the stock-out probability as an objective criterion. The probability of stock-out, p_r:

$$p_r = \int_{D_R > S_c} f(D_R)dD_R$$

This function is available in a tabulated form for a standard normal distribution $\mathcal{N}(0; \sigma)$. It is provided in Appendix A.2 in function of the parameter z defined as:

$$z = \frac{S_c - \bar{D}_R}{\sigma_{DR}} = \frac{S_s}{\sigma_{DR}}$$

After that the characteristics of the demand distribution during the replenishment time are determined, i.e. $\bar{D}_R$ and σDR, and a stock-out probability objective, p_r, is fixed, the safety stock, S_s, can be determined using the following procedure:

(1) Determine parameter z from Appendix A.1 on the basis of p_r
(2) Compute $S_s = z \times \sigma_{DR}$
(3) Compute $S_c = S_s + \bar{D}_R$

Example of safety stock calculation using the stock-out probability criterion

In this example, a stock-out probability objective of less than 5% is fixed. In addition, the variability of the demand per period D_p and of the replenishment time R are described by the discrete probability distributions given in Figs. 5.22 and 5.23.

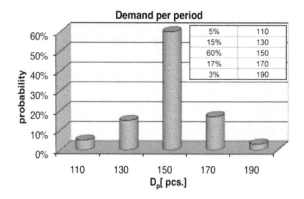

Fig. 5.22   Probability distribution of the demand per period.

The first step consists of characterising the two distributions using an approximation by a normal distribution. This lead to the results provided in Table 5.19.

The distribution of the demand D_R during the replenishment time can now be computed according to

$$D_R(\bar{R}\bar{D}_p; \sqrt{\bar{D}_p^2 \sigma_R^2 + \bar{R}\sigma_{D_p}{}^2}) = (2334; 721)$$

The 3-step method described above can now be applied.

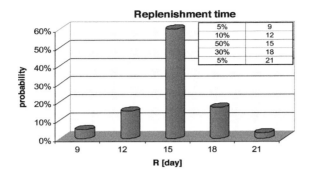

Fig. 5.23   Probability distribution of the replenishment time.

Table 5.19   Example distributions.

	D_p	R
mean	150	15.6
standard deviation	32	4.7

(1) Determine parameter z from Appendix A.1 on the basis of p_r. The value of $z = 1.64$ can be found in Appendix A.1
(2) Compute $S_s = z \times \sigma_{DR} = 1.64 \times 721 = 1182$
(3) Compute $S_c = S_s + \bar{D}_r = 1182 + 2334 = 3516$

In practice, these results will be rounded up to more workable values such as for example:

$$S_s = 1200, \ S_c = 3550$$

5.7.4 *Safety stock calculation using the order satisfaction level criterion*

With this approach, the safety stock is determined so as to fulfil an objective of order satisfaction. In other words, it is a service level criterion that determines the level of the safety stock. The order satisfaction level, p_c, is defined as follows:

$$p_r = 1 - \frac{1}{Q} \int_{D_R > S_c}^{\infty} (D_R - S_c) f(D_R) dD_R \qquad (5.32)$$

The function describing the non available quantity $Q0$ constitutes the critical element:

$$Q^0 = t_{D_R > S_c}^\infty f(D_R) dD_R$$

If $f(D_R)$ is normally distributed, the value of $Q0$ can be determined according to the following relation:

$$Q^0 = \int_{D_R > S_c}^\infty (D_R - S_c) f(D_R) dD_R = \sigma_{DR} \times E(z) \qquad (5.33)$$

Here, $E(z)$ is called the *service function*, and is given by:

$$E(z) = \int_z^\infty (x - z) f(x) dx$$

The service function $E(z)$ is available in tabulated form for a standard normal distribution $\mathcal{N}(0; \sigma)$. It is provided in Appendix A.2 in function of the parameter z defined as:

$$z = \frac{S_c - \bar{D}_R}{\sigma_{DR}} = \frac{S_s}{\sigma_{DR}} \qquad (5.34)$$

According to the previous development, the order satisfaction level can be reformulated as:

$$p_r = 1 - \frac{1}{Q} \int_{D_R > S_c}^\infty (D_R - S_c) f(D_R) dD_R = 1 - \frac{1}{Q} \sigma_{DR} E(z)$$

The value of the service function can consequently be computed according to:

$$E(z) = \frac{Q(1 - p_c)}{\sigma_{DR}} \qquad (5.35)$$

After that the characteristics of the demand distribution during the replenishment time are determined, i.e. $(\bar{D}_R)$ and σ_{DR} , and a order satisfaction level objective p_c is fixed, the safety stock S_s can be determined using the following procedure:

(1) Determine the value of the service function on the basis of Q and p_c
(2) Determine parameter z from Appendix A.2 on the basis of $E(z)$
(3) Compute $S_s = z \times \sigma_{DR}$
(4) Compute $S_c = S_s + \bar{D}_R$

Example of safety stock calculation using the order satisfaction level criterion

This example is based on the same example, and assume a service level objective of 98%. The order quantity is assumed to be $Q = 10000$. The characteristics of the distributions of the demand per period D_p and of the replenishment time R are given in Table 5.20.

Table 5.20 Example distributions — order satisfaction level criterion.

	D_p	R
mean	150	15.6
standard deviation	32	4.7

The distribution of the demand D_R during the replenishment time is again given as below.

$$D_R(\bar{R}\bar{D}_p; \sqrt{\bar{D}_p^2\sigma_R^2 + \bar{R}\sigma_{D_p}^2}) = (2334; 721)$$

The 4 step method described above can now be applied as described below:

(1) Determine the value of the service function $E(z)$ on the basis of Q and p_c.

$$E(z) = \frac{Q(1 - p_c)}{\sigma_{DR}} = \frac{10000(1 - 0.98)}{721} = 0.2774$$

(2) Determine parameter z from Appendix A.2 on the basis of $E(z)$. For $E(z) = 0.2774$ a value of $z = 0.287$ is found.
(3) Compute $S_s = z \times \sigma_{DR} = 0.287 \times 721 = 207$.
(4) Compute $S_c = S_s + \bar{D}_R = 207 + 2334 = 2541$.

In practice, these results will be rounded up to more workable values such as for example:

$$S_s = 200, \ S_c = 2550$$

5.7.5 *Conclusion*

Comparing the above-presented examples, it can be observed that the two performance criteria, stock-out probability and order satisfaction level, have different meanings. Assume that the annual demand is 100000 units. If the order quantity is 10000, this leads to 10 replenishment cycles per year. Assume also a fictive situation in which, due to the demand variability and other uncertainties, 10 units cannot be delivered at each cycle. This leads to following values of the two performance criteria.

- 100% stock-out
- 99.9% order satisfaction

Such an assessment might be given since the stock-out criterion does not consider the delivered quantity but put forward the missing quantities. However, the order satisfaction level has the characteristic of a relative criterion as it compares a missing quantity with an available one. In practice, data are easily available for the past. However it is much more difficult to foreseen any future situations. The methods described in this chapter might be applied to such cases since they try to integrate uncertainties. Finally, the reliability of forecast can also be integrated into the procedure so as to take into account this source of uncertainty too.

5.8   Chapter summary and coaching guideline

In this chapter, we discussed the fundamental elements and methods of inventory management with its role in manufacturing firms. Several inventory management methods are introduced according to their categories. The important notations to understand includes Economic Order Quantity, Economic Order Interval, and Reorder Point. The following subsections present example requirements extracted from our three-week coaching sessions.

5.8.1   *First week — Learning basic concepts*

General instruction

The board of director of your company has decided to launch an improvement project for material supply. The purpose is to establish preferential relationships and collaborative supply management with a few of main suppliers. The board wishes to study the possibility of replacing the traditional purchasing methods based on push MRP material flow by an appropriate inventory management method.

The Operations Manager has given you the mission to study and compare the performance of various inventory management methods that could be integrated in a future frame of contract with the supplier of a specific component.

Your objectives of this coaching session are:

- Understand and describe the methodology and procedure you intend to use for establishing a material supply using inventory management instead of MRP;
- Get a first version of a inventory management solution using the Reorder Point method.

Your tasks for this coaching session

- Check the availability of data you require for establishing a material management using the Reorder Point and PPB methods.
- Prepare and describe a material management plan using Reorder Point.
- Prepare and describe a material management plan using the PPB method.
- Obtain a material management solution using the Reorder Point method, and provide your observation on the results.

5.8.2 *Second week — Intermediary presentation*

The goal is to evaluate the performances of the two inventory management methods, Reorder point and PPB and accomplish a comparative analysis of the two methods. You should draw conclusion and recommendations concerning the method to be used in the future frame of contract of the company.

Your tasks for this coaching session

- Acquire the data and get a full version of a material management solution using the Reorder Point method and PPB method.
- Determine, for each method, the ordering cost, the inventory carrying cost and their sum for considering the current year.
- Draw a graphical representation of the inventory evolution of the current year.
- Explain the reasons for the observed differences between the methods.

- Describe the advantages and weaknesses of each method with regard to their integration in the frame of contact.
- Draw conclusion.

5.8.3 *Third week — Consolidating the whole concepts*

With the help of your high quality analysis that you provided us last week, the first contact with our supplier have been successful. They have shown a common will for finding more efficient material management methods. Consequently, the Operations Manager is also asking you to study more carefully the supply of the critical component and in particular to:

- Dimension the safety stock required for assuring a reliable supply using the Reorder Point method for the short term (current year).
- Suggest a long-term solution.

Your tasks for this coaching session

- Identify the required data.
- Determine the safety stock required in order to ensure the supply reliability objective specified by the company for the short-term vision. You can also suggest a relevant level of reliability objective to our company, based upon which you develop your method.
- Draw appropriate conclusions from this study and make recommendations to the Board of Directors concerning the short-term and long-term solution to be adopted for material supply.

Chapter 6

Just-In-Time and KANBAN Management

Looking at the historical development of operations management since the Second World War, two major directions can roughly be identified:

- The development and broad expansion of MRP, as a way to handle the complexity of manufacturing system that cannot be managed correctly by simple inventory replenishment approaches. Basically, MRP can be seen as a systematic procedure, based on a deterministic view of the system, and therefore essentially ignoring uncertainty, but with the capability of dealing with a very complex situation. Due to the complexity of the problem and the huge number of data to handle, MRP becomes in practice a black box with no transparency.
- The development of human centred approaches such as Just-In-Time (JIT) that aim at reducing complexity, increasing transparency.

Those two approaches, MRP and JIT, are fundamentally different. The first one, essentially developed in the western countries, is based on technology while the latter, mainly developed in Japan, relies on human involvement. Despite their opposite nature, MRP and JIT should not be looked at as being incompatible and/or conflicting ones. Both approaches have specific advantages and weakness as well as their own fields of use. They can also be intelligently combined in, so-called, hybrid approaches to production management. This chapter is structured around the following subjects aiming at providing knowledge about what are JIT and Lean material flow management, as well as bringing competencies on when and how to implement them.

6.1   Introduction to Just-In-Time material flow

Let us start by summarising the major evolution of the economic environment that manufacturing companies are facing.

- Increase of product variety;
- Decrease of product volume;
- Decrease of product life cycle;
- Reduced delivery delays;
- Sales price pressure;
- Increase of service quality (i.e. reliability of delivery).

These trends are primarily due to the global market and competition that companies have to deal with, while always putting forward their distinguishing advantages. The consequences of this business evolution on production & operations management are that:

- Rationalisation methods adapted to high volumes (heavy automation) become inappropriate;
- Planning methods based on medium term forecasts become inapplicable.

Therefore, it is preferable that management method and tools are adapted to such a situation, in particular:

- Improve the delivery flexibility without increasing tied-up capital;
- Satisfy market demand as quickly as possible, i.e. *Just-In-Time*;
- Reduce the costs, particularly the costs that do not contribute to adding value, i.e. the *hidden factory*.

This is what the Just-in-Time approach tries to do. Several definitions of Just-in-Time, JIT, can be found in the abundant literature on the subject. Among many definitions, within the scope of this book, we define it as "A production and logistics strategy based on an efficient management of material and information flows, with the purpose of responding to market requirements with maximum efficiency".

The most well-known principle of JIT concerns produce only what will be sold, at the right moment, with the required quality and in exact quantity.

It is noted that JIT can be seen and has been used as a:

- Global production philosophy;
- Strategy for production and logistics organisation;
- Management method;
- Group of management, planning and control techniques.

As stated above, JIT calls for simplification and transparency. It promotes also continuous improvement and the resolution of inefficiencies and malfunctioning instead of creating buffers in order to cover them. This is an important philosophical element, which often corresponds to a cultural attitude and a major change.

JIT advocates a permanent fight against any activity and cost that does not add value for the customer. Subsequently, it calls for the elimination, or reducing as much as possible all administrative tasks, centralised hierarchical controls. Instead of such inefficiencies, it looks for simplification and the delegation of responsibility to the shop-floor. This ballast of non-value-adding activities is sometimes called the *hidden factory*. JIT wants to reduce it as much as possible.

In order to reach the previous objectives, JIT uses a global framework (Fig. 6.1) based on two major elements: reducing the lead-times and improving the flexibility of the production system. To do so, several ways and appropriate tools are available. A number of them are indicated in Fig. 6.1.

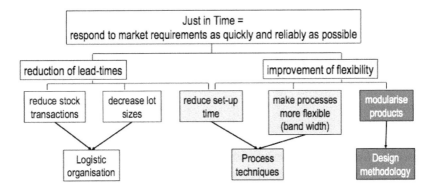

Fig. 6.1   Global JIT framework.

Finally, JIT is constituted of several building blocks that concern product & process design, logistics, work environment and human aspects. Implementing JIT requires taking all these issues into account simultaneously considering human, technological and organisational aspects.

6.2   Pull versus push material flow management

One of the main objectives of JIT is to create efficient flows of material and information. JIT calls for simplicity, transparency and delegation of responsibility. In order to understand clearly the JIT, a distinction between a push and a pull flow must firstly be made. In a push material flow, production orders (PO) are launched in a production centre according to computed requirements based on forecasts. This is how the MRP approach works. The material then goes into inventory where it may wait until a true requirement appears since forecasts cannot figure out the future demands with 100% reliability. Therefore, the material is pushed into inventory according to the forecasts. Due to the lack of reliability of the forecasts and other uncertainties, we often find a situation in which critical items are missing when they are required while non-necessary ones are piling up in inventory. This results in high inventory costs and low delivery reliability. Figure 6.2 illustrates the organisation of a push material flow managed by MRP.

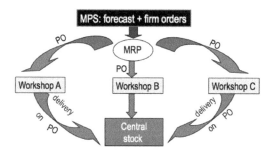

Fig. 6.2   Push material flows.

In a pull material flow, production is launched when the requirement appears at the downstream workstation, i.e. at the customer location. Thus, production is launched only to satisfy the known requirement of the customer. Such a close relationship between supplier and customer promotes transparency and motivation for the production centre. This is the opposite of the MRP-based push approach in which the customers' actual requirement is still not known when the production starts.

In Fig. 6.3 dual supplier-customer relationship is reproduced in sequence along the value-adding chain, leading to a material flow going downstream and an information flow (order for delivery) running upstream.

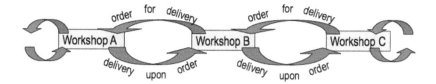

Fig. 6.3 Pull material flows.

A pull flow management might not necessarily lead to a low inventory concept. For the purpose of running the production while keeping the stock level at minimum, each workstation must be able to react quickly to upcoming requirements, which informs necessary items in the customer buffer stock. Such management with low intermediate buffer stock is called *direct logistics flow*. The following definitions summarise the different management methods.

- Production on down-stream demand: pull flow;
- Production without intermediate stocks: direct logistics flow;
- Production on centrally planned production orders: push flow;
- Production with intermediate stocks, intermediary transport: indirect logistics flow.

The direct logistic flow requires several conditions to be satisfied. In particular, a high level of reactivity is mandatory which should be supported by small lot sizes, short setup-times, and short transportation times. The short reaction implies also short production lead-times. In a real situation, with stochastic behaviour, the throughput-time increases in a non-linear way with the increase of utilisation rates larger than 80% (Fig. 6.4).

This implicitly assess that production centres should never be loaded above approximately 80% if the direct logistics flow approach is chosen.

This runs against commonly shared thinking in production which tries to minimise the production cost only based on the utilisation rate of machines. Such a shortsighted cost computation often ignores the cost of useless inventory and poor delivery reliability. The effort of achieving short reaction time and short lead-time needs for extra investment in production operating methods. However, this extra cost shall be compensated afterward by reduced inventory carrying costs and customer dissatisfaction.

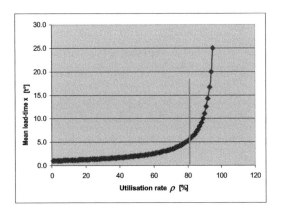

Fig. 6.4   Utilisation rate versus throughput efficiency.

6.3   The KANBAN method

The KANBAN method was originally developed beginning of the 1950s in Japan by Mr Ohno at the Toyota Motor Company and started to be really implemented around 1958. This approach seeks simplification, transparency and delegation of responsibility to the operational level, i.e. the shop floor. KANBAN means "card" in Japanese. Nowadays, the word KANBAN is being used with different meanings, as listed below:

- As flow regularisation method using JIT philosophy;
- Meaning organisation and management method of workshops based on a card circulation system;
- Referring to industrial or planning management method.

In all cases, the objective of the approach is a simple, transparent, visual management method so as to ensure a direct logistics flow.

6.3.1   *Basic principles of KANBAN*

The principles of the KANBAN method are given below:

- Produce only products that are required by the customer;
- Produce them exactly when they are required;
- Produce them exactly in the required quantity.

For the purpose of implementing such production principles, the following rules should be respected by workshops.

- An upstream workstation must only produce what is asked from its downstream workstations;
- The most downstream workstation must only produce what the end customers ask for.

When two adjacent work centres are linked by KANBANs, this is called a KANBAN loop. When several adjacent work centres are linked by KAN-BANs, it is called a KANBAN chain.

A KANBAN container, which i s the medium of material flows, represents a fixed quantity of items transported from supplier workshops to downstream customers. This quantity is called the KANBAN size and constitutes an important design parameter of a KANBAN system (loop or chain). A KANBAN size is never changed during production and must be strictly respected. The KANBAN method uses a medium of information transfer so that information is rapidly transferred from downstream to upstream. There are different ways of transferring the information from one customer work centre to its supplier according to the type of the medium. In all cases, the main criteria of choosing the information transporter are *simplicity* and *transparency*.

In practice, the most often used ways of KANBAN information transfer are cards (the KANBAN cards). When cards are used, they are transferred from customer to supplier, and returned back to the customers with the corresponding items. A predefined and limited number of cards are circulating between the adjacent work centres. The conceptual model is illustrated in Fig. 6.5.

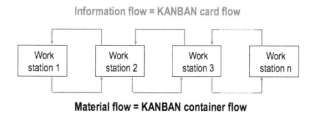

Fig. 6.5   KANBAN loop.

Figure 6.6 illustrates the case of a KANBAN loop between two work centres using cards to transfer information from customer to supplier. When the cards, sent from the customer, are arrived at the supplier's work centre, they are placed at a specific location, such as *Chart 4*, meaning a precise location at the supplier work centre. The KANBAN container which shall be sent to the customer contains exact number of items of the KANBAN size. At the customer work centre, when the KANBAN container is received. Similarly, the container is stored at a precise and unique location (*Stock B3*, in this example).

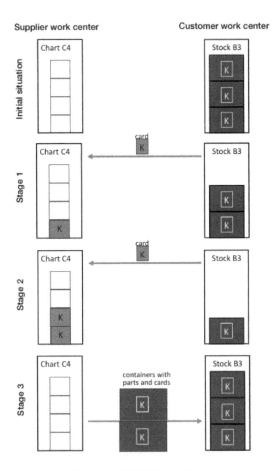

Fig. 6.6   KANBAN method.

At the initial situation from which the first KANBAN loop starts, the customer buffer stock is fully filled (Fig. 6.6, initial situation), and there is no cards at the supplier location. The following steps are operated at both production sites after the production starts:

- Stage 1: As soon as all the items of the first KANBAN container are used, the corresponding KANBAN card is immediately sent to the supplier work centre and placed on chart C4. At this stage, there is 1 card in chart C4 of the supplier and 2 KANBANs in buffer stock B3 of the customer. The supplier work centre is not yet allowed to start production (for reasons that will be discussed later).
- Stage 2: When all the items of the second KANBAN are used at the customer work centre, the corresponding card is immediately sent to the supplier and placed above the first card on chart C4. There are now 2 cards in chart C4 (at the supplier) and 1 KANBAN in buffer stock *B3* (at the customer).
- Stage 3: We now assume that the supplier work centre is allowed to start production when 2 cards are present on chartC4 and we he/she decides to do so. The exact quantity of 2 KANBAN sizes items are then produced at the supplier work centre. The 2 KANBAN containers filled with the items, as well as the two cards, are delivered without delay to the customer, and placed in buffer stock *B3*. There are 0 KANBAN card on chart C4 at the supplier work centre and 3 KANBAN containers in buffer stock of the customer *B3* (now refilled).

This process is iterated at a frequency that depends on the demand from the customer work centre. In practice, it also happens that cards are replaced by strictly labelled empty containers for the information transfer. In this case, only the containers are circulating between the customer and supplier to regulate the KANBAN loop.

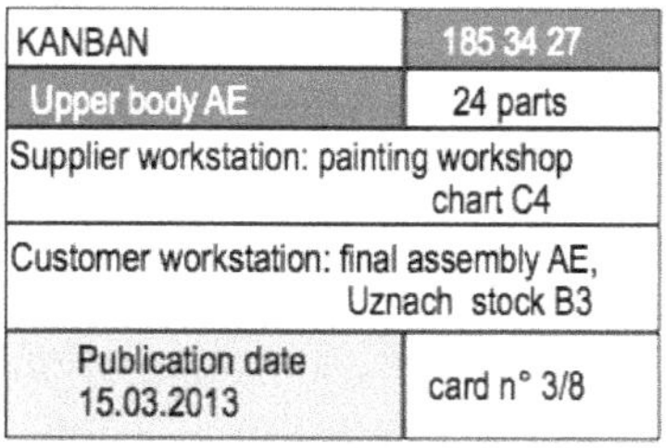

KANBAN	185 34 27
Upper body AE	24 parts
Supplier workstation: painting workshop chart C4	
Customer workstation: final assembly AE, Uznach stock B3	
Publication date 15.03.2013	card n° 3/8

Fig. 6.7   KANBAN card example.

A KANBAN card must contain a number of data, as illustrated in Fig. 6.7:

- Item number (if possible with a picture of the item);
- Item description;
- KANBAN size (number of items per KANBAN container);
- Location at the supplier work centre;
- Location at the customer work centre;
- Card number.

6.3.2 *Operating a KANBAN loop*

To ensure good performances of using KANBAN in production operations, some rules must be strictly followed:

- Produce only the quantity specified by the cards;
- Strictly respect the quantities per KANBAN;
- Immediately circulate the KANBAN containers and the cards;
- Limit the number of item types managed by KANBAN to a maximum of approximately 10 by work centre;
- Adjust the number of KANBANs according to the requirements and performance improvements.

To operate the KANBAN loop efficiently, while allowing to the supplier work center a certain degree of freedom in decision-making, management levels are defined. Generally, three levels are considered:

(1) Green level: it defines the minimum number of KANBAN cards required for starting production (at the supplier work centre).
(2) Orange level: this level defines the maximum number of KANBAN cards allowed before starting production (at the supplier work centre).
(3) Red level: Total number of KANBAN in the loop.

Figure 6.8 exhibits an example of a supplier workstation chart for three items (items numbers 37'350'02, 37'360'01 and 37'360'12).

As previously mentioned, the quantity available at the customer work centre can be known on the supplier chart. A supplier work centre can assume this by measuring the distance between Red level and the actual number of KANBAN cards on the chart area.

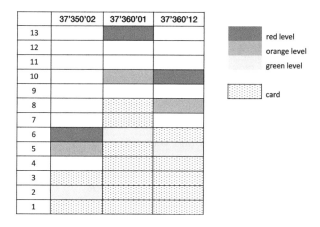

Fig. 6.8   Example KANBAN chart with levels.

According to the KANBAN production rule, the supplier work centre is capable of deciding the launching moment of production respecting the following priority rules:

- Priority 1: Launch production of items between the red and orange levels in decreasing order of priority (closest to the red level first).
- Priority 2: Launch items between orange and green levels. The supplier work centre can flexibly make decision on production launch if the cards are within this range. A priority rule shall not necessarily be applied among these KANBAN cards. However, it is possible to give priority to the card which is closest to the orange level, and then dealing with the others in decreasing priority.
- It is not allowed for the supplier center to launch production of items below the green level.

Conditions for successful KANBAN implementation

A KANBAN process requires some conditions to be successfully implemented. Besides the human and training aspects, it can be applied well under a fairly regular and continuous demand rate. The performances of KANBAN decrease when the demand rates are irregular. In addition, it does not make much sense if the demand rate is very low. As a general rule of implementation, a KANBAN size should not be designed to cover more than (approximately) 5 days of demand (1 business week). Otherwise, the frequency of KANBAN circulation between the customer and supplier becomes too low.

It is worth mentioning that other typical conditions of JIT must also be satisfied for the purpose of having a fully successful KANBAN implementation, such as reduction of setup times, process reliability, material flow oriented layout, standardisation and modularisation of products and processes, as well as flexibility and versatility of workers.

6.3.3   *Characteristics of a KANBAN loop*

Toyota formula

For the purpose of managing efficiently the KANBAN loop, the first condition to be satisfied concerns finding an optimal KANBAN size. When Toyota introduced KANBAN to their manufacturing operations management, the company created a generic formula to compute the optimal number of KANBAN cards. The prevailing assumptions include that the demand rate is constant for each period over the planning horizon. In such a situation, the *number of KANBAN cards*, N_c can be defined according to the following formula:

$$N_c = \frac{Demand\ rate \times Lead\text{-}time \times [1 + Policy\ variable]}{Container\ size}$$

Here, the policy variable may concern a safety stock policy or similar variables which influence the net requirement, and can be presented as a factor (%).

The formula is generalised as below (Eq. (6.1)), and will be referenced in the context of this chapter.

$$N_c = \frac{DR(1+s)}{K} \tag{6.1}$$

where:

N_c: number of KANBAN card,
D: constant demand rate,
R: lead-time, or refreshment time,
s: policy variable, such as safety stock,
K: KANBAN container size.

Before discussing possible approaches to dimensioning a KANBAN loop, let us examine the behaviour of the loop over one replenishment circle.

Assumptions

In order to compute the evolution of WIP at the customer work centre in a KANBAN loop, we should first of all understand the assumptions considered in implementing the system. The model presented below is formed under the following assumption.

- KANBAN management levels are represented as L_1 (Green Level), L_2 (Orange Level), and L_3 (Red Level).
- Launching KANBAN level L* represents the level at which the production is launched at the supplier workstation.
- A constant demand rate $D = 1$ is assumed with replenishment time $R = 2$ periods.
- For the sake of simplicity, the production set-up time is zero for all operations. As soon as a KANBAN container is delivered, production can be immediately launched.
- The KANBAN lead-time is zero. That means, a KANBAN card returned to a work centre at time t will immediately initiate production at time t. It is possible to implement other values of KANBAN lead-time. For example, if the KANBAN lead-time is equal to 1, a KANBAN card returned to a work centre at time t is used to initiate production at time $(t + 1)$.
- There is no limitations on the supplier capacity. The supply lead-time will be guaranteed regardless of the number of KANBAN cards to work on.

Based on the above-mentioned assumptions, Fig. 6.9 describes the evolution of the number of KANBAN cards at the supplier location (dotted line) and that of the KANBAN containers at the customer location (solid line), which can implicitly represent the WIP level at the customer centre. To simplify the graphical representation, the discrete nature of the KANBAN process is not shown; instead, a continuous process is assumed, which is equivalent to assuming a KANBAN size equal to 1.

The evolution can be observed from four points:

(1) At the time of initiation
(2) When the level of cards reaches L_1

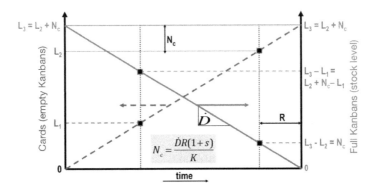

Fig. 6.9   Evolution of WIP in a KANBAN loop.

(3) When the level of cards reaches L_2
(4) When the level of cards reaches L_3

These points are more detailed in Table 6.1.

Table 6.1   KANBAN level interpretation.

Supplier: card level	Customer Containers	Comment
0	L_3	At initiation time only, never happens again later
L_1	$L_3 - L_1$	Maximum possible number of KANBANs after initiation
L_2	$L_3 - L_2$	Minimum number of KANBAN if loop managed correctly
L_3	0	Does never happen if loop managed correctly

Now let us consider the discrete nature of the process by taking the KANBAN container size into account. The following definitions are used for our illustrations.

- KANBAN management levels L_1, L_2, L_3
- Launching KANBAN level L^*
- Constant demand rate $D = 1$ KANBAN/period
- Constant replenishment time $R = (L_3 - L_2)/D = 2$ period

Three different launching decisions can be considered, which are characterised as below:

- Case (A) $L^* = \frac{(L_1+L_2)}{2}$: launching decisions are always made when the KANBAN cards are between $L1$ and L_2.
- Case (B) $L^* = L_1$: launching decisions are always made as soon as KANBAN cards reach L_1.
- Case (C) $L^* = L_2$: launching decisions are made at last-minute when KANBAN cards reach L_2.

We compute the following values for the purpose of learning the evolution of WIP in each case:

- Minimum level of WIP: W_{min}
- Maximum level of WIP: W_{max}
- Average WIP: W_{avg}

The relations which describe a general case, $L^* = L^*$ can be described as below:

$$W_{min} = L_3 - L^* - (L_3 - L_2) = L_2 - L^* \tag{6.2}$$

$$W_{max} = W_{min} + L^* = L_2 - L^* + L^* = L_2 \tag{6.3}$$

$$W_{avg} = \frac{W_{max} + W_{min}}{2} = \frac{L_2 + (L_2 - L^*)}{2} = L_2 - \frac{L^*}{2} \tag{6.4}$$

Now, each of three cases are graphically illustrated.

**Evolution of WIP in the Kanban loop,
case (A) $L^* = 1/2(L_1 + L_2)$**

The following relations describe the WIP evolution in this case.

$$W_{min} = L_2 - L^* = L_2 - \frac{L_1 + L_2}{2} = \frac{L_2 - L_1}{2} \tag{6.5}$$

$$W_{max} = L_2 \tag{6.6}$$

$$W_{avg} = L_2 - \frac{L^*}{2} = L_2 - \frac{L_1 + L_2}{4} = \frac{3L_2 - L_1}{4} \tag{6.7}$$

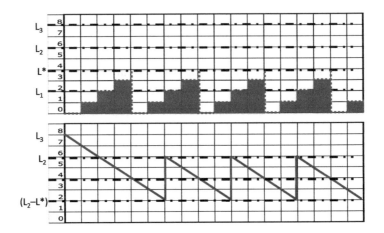

Fig. 6.10 Evolution of WIP in a KANBAN loop: case (A) with $L^* = 1/2(L_1 + L_2)$.

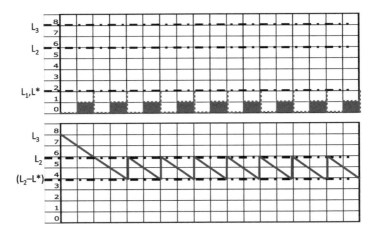

Fig. 6.11 Evolution of WIP in a KANBAN loop: case (B) with $L^* = L_1$.

Evolution of WIP in the Kanban loop, case (B) $L^* = L_1$

The following relations describe the WIP evolution in this case.

$$W_{min} = L_2 - L^* = L_2 - L_1 \tag{6.8}$$

$$W_{max} = L_2 \tag{6.9}$$

$$W_{avg} = L_2 - \frac{L^*}{2} = L_2 - \frac{L_1}{2} = \frac{2L_2 - L_1}{2} \tag{6.10}$$

Evolution of WIP in the Kanban loop, case (C) $L^* = L_2$

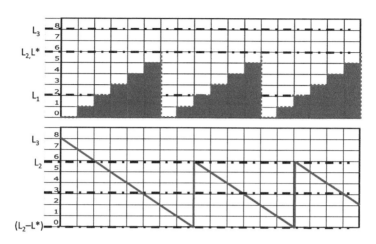

Fig. 6.12   Evolution of WIP in a KANBAN loop: case (C) with $L^* = L_2$.

The following relations describe the WIP evolution in this case.

$$W_{min} = L_2 - L^* = L_2 - L_2 = 0 \qquad (6.11)$$

$$W_{max} = L_2 \qquad (6.12)$$

$$W_{avg} = L_2 - \frac{L^*}{2} = L_2 - \frac{L_2}{2} = \frac{L_2}{2} \qquad (6.13)$$

Summary

From the above-presented three cases, the following conclusions can be obtained:

- The highest initial level of WIP is reached only at the initiation time $(t = 0)$, and never happens again afterward;
- Whatever the launching level L^* is, the WIP level after delivery W_{max} remains unchanged;
- The WIP level just before delivery W_{min} depends on the actual launching level L^* and decreases with increasing L^*.

It is clear that the most critical situation occurs when level $L2$ is reached. In this case, the remaining quantity at the customer location is $N = L_3 - L_2$. This quantity must be sufficient to cover for the requirements during the replenishment time R. This is similar to a reorder point in inventory management. With the previous assumption of constant demand rate D, levels L_2 and L_3 are related by the following equation:

$$N = L_3 - L_2 = \frac{DR}{K}(1+s)$$

where $s > 0$ is a safety factor. In practice, since both D and R vary stochastically, a statistical approach shall be used to compute N. The approach is similar to that used for computing a safety stock in reorder point based inventory management. In order to determine the three management levels L_1, L_2, and L_3, let us define the corresponding quantity of items by Q_1, Q_2 and Q_3 respectively. The basis used for computing these quantities are indicated in Fig. 6.13.

	37'360'01	L_3: total number of KANBAN in the loop
13		
12		• quantity Q_3 determined based on the response time for the delivery of the launching quantity Q_2
11		
10		L_2: maximum level for launching production
9		
8		• maximum value of quantity Q_2 based on:
7		1) launching flexibility provided by (Q_2-Q_1) and 2) maximum increase of total cost with respect to EOQ
6		
5		L_1: minimum level for launching production
4		
3		• minimum value of quantity Q_1 based on: 1) minimum ratio between production time and the setup time and
2		2) maximum increase of total cost with respect EOQ
1		

Fig. 6.13   Basis for computing the KANBAN management levels.

6.4   Dimensioning KANBAN level and container size

This section describes a method for dimensioning KANBAN management parameters such as the total number of KANBAN cards, the KANBAN container size, as well as the number of cards of each level (Levels 1, 2, and 3).

The following parameters and symbols are used in our mathematical model:

N_{tot}: total requirements over the modelling horizon H,
c_L: fixed cost of launching order,
p: value of the item after operation,

r_c: inventory carrying cost over the horizon H,

c: production cost per unit,

e: acceptable relative increase of total cost,

T_s: setup time,

T_t: transport time,

δ: min value between production time,

t: hourly rate of production,

ΔT: temporary launching flexibility (between Q_1 and Q_2),

$R(Q_2)$: response time for delivery of launching quantity Q_2,

dR/dt: production rate,

dD/dt: demand rate,

K: KANBAN size,

n_k: total number of KANBAN in the loop.

The proposed procedure for computing the three management levels consists of the following steps.

(1) Determine the optimal economic order quantity Q_0;

$$Q_0 = \text{EOQ} = \sqrt{\frac{2N_{tot}c_L}{pr_c}}$$

(2) Determine the total cost associated to Q_0;

$$C_0 = N_{tot}p + \frac{Q_0}{2}pr_c + \frac{N_{tot}}{Q_0}c_L$$

(3) Determine the quantity Q_1;

$$Q_1 = \max\left[Q_0 - \sqrt{\frac{eC_0Q_0^3}{N_{tot}c_L}};\ \delta T_s\frac{t}{c}\right] = \max\left[Q_0 - \sqrt{\frac{eC_0Q_0^3}{N_{tot}c_L}};\ \delta T_s R\right]$$

(4) Determine the quantity Q_2;

$$Q_2 = \min\left[Q_0 + \sqrt{\frac{eC_0Q_0^3}{N_{tot}c_L}};\ Q_1 + \Delta T\frac{N_{tot}}{H}\right]$$

$$= \min\left[Q_0 + \sqrt{\frac{eC_0Q_0^3}{N_{tot}c_L}};\ Q_1 + \Delta TD\right]$$

(5) Determine the quantity Q_3;

$$Q_3 = Q_2 + R(Q_2)\frac{N_{tot}}{H} = Q_2 + R(Q_2)D$$

$$R(Q_2) = T_s + \frac{Q_2}{R} + T_t$$

(6) Determine the KANBAN size which satisfies approximately the following conditions at the same time;

$$K \cong \frac{Q_1}{n_1} \quad \text{with } n_1 \in N[2;5]$$

$$K \cong \frac{Q_2 - Q_1}{n_2} \quad \text{with } n_2 \in N[3;7]$$

where N is the set of natural number.

(7) Compute of the number of KANBANs in the loop;

$$n_k \cong \frac{Q_3}{K}$$

(8) Finally, compute the management levels;

$$L_1 \cong \frac{Q_1}{K}, \ L_2 \cong \frac{Q_2}{K}, \ L_3 \cong \frac{Q_3}{K} \qquad (6.14)$$

Dimensioning a KANBAN loop can be achieved through different ways, either according to a heuristic method or based on an optimisation formula. The above-mentioned procedure explains how to determine the management parameters by a pragmatic way including practical constraints as factors. The resulting values ensure operating the KANBAN loop under a given situation. Following the general guideline behind JIT, it is recommended to continue observing and measuring the performance related with material flows in order to continually improve the efficiency.

The performance of a KANBAN loop is directly related to the conditions in which the loop operates. It is therefore important to be aware of the critical factors which compose the conditions, and of their influence on the KANBAN loop performances. The following list summarises commonly understood influencing factors:

- Demand stability;
- Flexibility and variety of competence of the employees;
- Reliability and stability of processes;
- Setup times.

Even though the level of sensitivity might be different from one case to another, each specific case of KANBAN management demonstrates a certain range of performance variation in response to the modification of those factors.

6.5 Review of main methods of managing material flows

In this subsection, we summarise the three main methods which have been presented so far. Each method is illustrated using the symbols presented in Fig. 6.14.

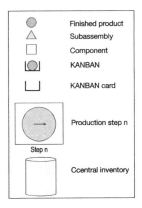

Fig. 6.14   Legend of symbols.

Method 1: Centralised inventory control

The centralised inventory management method, Fig. 6.15, is characterised by a material flow pulled from the demand through a reorder point inventory management policy. All items are kept in the inventory. often in a centralised location. Forecasting is not mandatory for operational control. Production Orders (PO) are launched by a central planning according to replenishment policies.

Method 2: MRP

This approach, presented in Fig. 6.16, is based on an anticipation of the requirements of each item. Consequently, the material is pushed (generally into a central inventory) according to a demand forecasting. POs are launched by the central planning according to the MRP mechanism. MRP requires reliable demand forecasts, which is based on an accurate BOM.

Review of the inventory control method

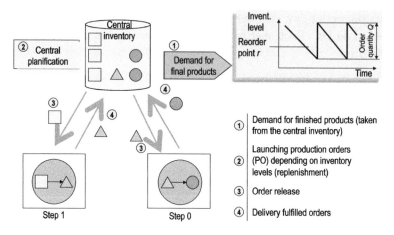

Fig. 6.15   Inventory management method.

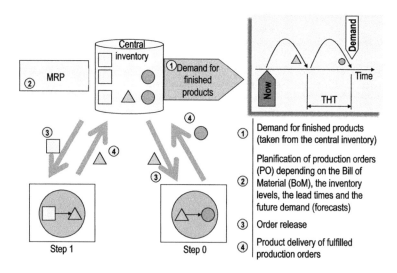

Fig. 6.16   MRP based approach.

Method 3: JIT, KANBAN

In this approach, the materials are *pulled* from the requirement for production. It uses a decentralised KANBAN control for managing the material flows, which is different from a centralised inventory control. As illustrated in Fig. 6.17, it can be seen as a series of customer-supplier relations. Instead of planning orders, the production is launched locally according to a decision made by the supplier work centre while continually referring the KANBAN card level.

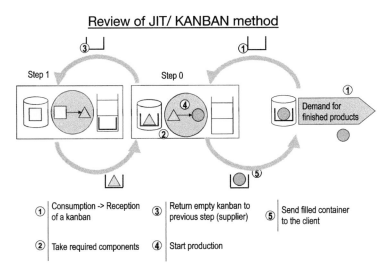

Fig. 6.17 JIT, KANBAN method.

6.6 Comparison of the main material flow management methods and conclusion

The above-presented approaches differ in terms of performances, strengths and weaknesses with respects to a given condition. The key question is therefore to know when to use one instead of the other. It is difficult to conclude with a general assessment without considering the particularities that each company is facing. Different situations can be found depending on the market, product, and product life cycle. It is important to understand the general positioning of the three methods considering the volume of demand and requirements for flexibility (in response to market changes and product variation). For instance, the central inventory control might be applicable to almost all of the cases but often at the expense of relatively high inventory carrying cost. Subsequently, it might be an interesting option for managing low value items with regular demand.

The main characteristics of the three approaches are summarised below.

Inventory control

- Simple concept;
- Focused on the optimisation of management parameters in order to reach a target service level (delivery reliability) at minimum cost (stock level).

MRP

- POs planned in a central planning department based on usual MRP process;
- Planning parameters include independent demand, bill of materials, throughput times, stock, and WIP levels. Most MRP systems use unlimited capacity;
- In order to be used efficiently, MRP requires reliable demand forecasts, precise and stable throughput times, detailed BoM, rigorous maintenance of the engineering data.

JIT, KANBAN

- Main goal of JIT/KANBAN is to perform high delivery reliability at minimum cost based on pull material flows;
- Launching operation is initiated by the execution of a downstream operation (pull) in a decentralised way;
- Implementation of KANBAN requires mastering processes and quality, decentralisation and delegation of responsibility, continuous improvement.

Several research results commonly accept that the MRP based method is more suitable for managing low, irregular demand and a high level of product variety whereas the JIT/KANBAN method is more advantageous when the product demand and processes are stable. Nevertheless, according to the observation in an aggregate way, the majority of today's manufacturing companies is positioned in the intermediary situation. Since neither approaches are completely satisfying their specific requirement, firms are progressively looking for a combined solution, which allows them to take advantage of strengths while minimising negative effects from both. It has entailed the development of hybrid production systems, the so called *hybrid systems*, which integrate MRP, JIT/KANBAN, as well as the inventory management methods suitable for the combined control.

Several methods can be categorised into the hybrid approach, such as Vertically Integrated Hybrid Systems, Horizontally Integrated Hybrid Systems, CONstant Work In Progress (CONWIP), or Double Speed Single Production Line (DSSPL), to mention a few, which will not be discussed in detail in the context of this book.

Appendix

A.1 Stock-out probability for normal distribution

Table A.1 illustrates the stock-out probability for normal distribution.

Table A.1   Stock-out probability for normal distribution.

z	$G(z)$	z	$G(z)$	z	$G(z)$	z	$G(z)$
0.00	0.50000	1.05	0.14686	2.05	0.02018	3.10	0.00097
0.05	0.48006	1.10	0.13567	2.10	0.01786	3.15	0.00082
0.10	0.46017	1.15	0.12507	2.15	0.01578	3.20	0.00069
0.15	0.44038	1.20	0.11507	2.20	0.01390	3.25	0.00058
0.20	0.42074	1.25	0.10565	2.25	0.01222	3.30	0.00048
0.25	0.40129	1.30	0.09680	2.30	0.01072	3.35	0.00040
0.30	0.38209	1.35	0.08851	2.35	0.00939	3.40	0.00034
0.35	0.36317	1.40	0.08076	2.40	0.00820	3.45	0.00028
0.40	0.34458	1.45	0.07353	2.45	0.00714	3.50	0.00023
0.45	0.32636	1.50	0.06681	2.50	0.00621	3.55	0.00019
0.50	0.30854	1.55	0.06057	2.55	0.00539	3.60	0.00016
0.55	0.29116	1.60	0.05480	2.60	0.00466	3.65	0.00013
0.60	0.27425	1.65	0.04947	2.65	0.00402	3.70	0.00011
0.65	0.25785	1.70	0.04457	2.70	0.00347	3.75	0.00009
0.70	0.24196	1.75	0.04006	2.75	0.00298	3.80	0.00007
0.75	0.22663	1.80	0.03593	2.80	0.00256	3.85	0.00006
0.80	0.21186	1.85	0.03216	2.85	0.00219	3.90	0.00005
0.85	0.19766	1.90	0.02872	2.90	0.00187	3.95	0.00004
0.90	0.18406	1.95	0.02559	2.95	0.00159	4.00	0.00003
0.95	0.17106	2.00	0.02275	3.00	0.00135		
1.00	0.15866			3.05	0.00114		

A.2 Service function

The objective is to determine the level of order satisfaction P_C, defined by:

$$P_c = \frac{Q}{V_d} = \frac{Q}{Q + L^o} = 1 - \frac{L^o}{Q + L^o}$$

$$P_C \cong 1 - L^o Q$$

where:

Q = available volume for delivery,
V_d = volume of demand,
$L^o = V_d - Q$ = non-available volume.

We want to determine L^o assuming that the statistical distribution of demand, N_R, during the time interval $t = [0, R$ can be represented by a continuous law whose probability density function is $f(N_R)$. L^o is a function of S, $L^o(S)$, representing the available volume at $t = 0$. The expression of the function $L^o(S)$ is the following:

$$L^o(S) = \int_S^\infty (N_R - S)f(N_R)dN_R \qquad (A.1)$$

$$\text{with} \quad f(N_R) = N(\bar{R}, \sigma_{N_R}) = \frac{1}{\sqrt{2\pi\sigma_{N_R}^2}}e^{-(N_R-\bar{R})2/2\sigma_{N_R}^2}$$

The following variables shall be replaced:

$$x = \frac{1}{\sigma_{N_R}}(N_R - \bar{R}), \ z = \frac{1}{\sigma_{N_R}}(S - \bar{R})$$

which result:

$$N_R = \bar{R} + \sigma_{N_R}x, \ S = \bar{R} + \sigma_{N_R}z \qquad (A.2)$$

According to characteristic a) of the normal distribution, the variable x has a normal distribution $f(x)$ defined by:

$$f(x) = N(\bar{x}, \sigma_x) = \frac{1}{\sqrt{2\pi\sigma_x^2}}e^{-(x-\bar{x})2/2\sigma_x^2}$$

$$\bar{x} = -\frac{\bar{R}}{\sigma_{N_R}} + \frac{1}{\sigma_{N_R}}\bar{R} = 0, \ \sigma_x = \frac{1}{\sigma_{N_R}}\sigma_{N_R} = 1$$

which derives:

$$f(x) = N(0, 1) = \frac{1}{\sqrt{2\pi}}e^{-x^2/2}$$

which is a standard distribution. On the other hand, by replacing x by its expression according to N_R, we obtain:

$$f(x) = \frac{1}{\sqrt{2\pi}} e^{\frac{-(N_R - \bar{R})^2}{2\sigma N_R}} = \sigma_{N_R} f(N_R) \tag{A.3}$$

By replacing N_R, S, $f(N_R)$ in Eq. (A.1), we obtain:

$$L^o(S) = \int_{\frac{1}{\sigma N_R}(S - \bar{R})}^{\infty} (\bar{R} + \sigma_{N_R} x - \bar{R} - \sigma_{N_R} z) \frac{1}{\sigma_{N_R}} f(x) \sigma_{N_R} dx$$

$$L^o(S) = \sigma_{N_R} \int_z^{\infty} (x - z) f(x) dx = \sigma_{N_R} E(z)$$

where $E(z) = \int_z^{\infty} (x - z) f(x) dx$ is the service function. $E(z)$ can be determined by:

$$E(z) = \int_z^{\infty} (x - z) \frac{1}{\sqrt{2\pi}} e^{-x^2/2} dx \tag{A.4}$$

$$E(z) = \frac{1}{\sqrt{2\pi}} \left[\int_z^{\infty} x e^{-x2/2} dx - z \int_z^{\infty} e^{-x^2/2} dx \right] \tag{A.5}$$

with $t = \frac{x}{\sqrt{2}}$, $x = \sqrt{2}t$, $dx = \sqrt{2}dt$.

$$E(z) = \frac{1}{\sqrt{2\pi}} \int_{z/\sqrt{2}}^{\infty} \sqrt{2} t e^{-t^2} \sqrt{2} dt - \frac{z}{\sqrt{2\pi}} \int_{z/\sqrt{2}}^{\infty} e^{-t^2} \sqrt{2} dt \tag{A.6}$$

$$E(z) = \frac{\sqrt{2}}{\sqrt{\pi}} \int_{z/\sqrt{2}}^{\infty} t e^{-t^2} dt - \frac{z}{\sqrt{\pi}} \int_{z/\sqrt{2}}^{\infty} e^{-t^2} dt \tag{A.7}$$

$$E(z) = \frac{\sqrt{2}}{\sqrt{\pi}} \left\| -\frac{1}{2} e^{-t^2} \right\|_{z/\sqrt{2}}^{\infty} - \frac{z}{2} erfc(z/\sqrt{2}) \tag{A.8}$$

Then, $erfc(t) = \frac{2}{\sqrt{\pi}} \int_t^{\infty} e^{-y^2} dy$ is an inverse error function.

$$E(z) = \frac{1}{\sqrt{2\pi}} e^{-z2/2} - \frac{z}{2} erfc(z/\sqrt{2})$$

The service function $E(z)$ can be represented as below:

$$E(z) = \frac{1}{\sqrt{2\pi}} e^{-z^2/2} - \frac{z}{2} erfc(z/\sqrt{2}) \tag{A.9}$$

Some computation results are given in Table A.2.

Table A.2   Service function.

z	$E(z)$
0.0	0.3989
0.2	0.3069
0.4	0.2304
0.6	0.1687
0.8	0.1202
1.0	0.0833
1.2	0.0561
1.4	0.0367
1.6	0.0232
1.8	0.0143
2.0	0.0085
2.2	0.0049
2.4	0.0027
2.6	0.0015
2.8	0.0008
3.0	0.0004

A.3   Former coaches' experience

Tian Cheng

Although I attended the same course in the previous year as a student, I greatly appreciate the chance to work as a coach for the Production Management course at EPFL during autumn semester 2015. Compared to the role as a student, a coach needs not only to prepare the course materials, but also to be able to access subtle estrangement influencing the team performance. Hereinafter, I would like to share some personal experiences and thoughts related to the coaching sessions of the course and hope that it could be useful to facilitate your future coaching sessions.

As you might notice, the production of a physical product is complicated, and is one of the important processes in a business. Basic knowledge or experience about production management can be very useful for students who will soon step into an enterprise, work in a team and might be in charge of production schedules in the future. The main focus of the coaching sessions is the team project which forms the practical part of the course. This project takes existing data from a well-known product on the market as an example to simulate its production management processes. Although all given conditions are manipulated, the project really helps students to understand both definitions used in the daily production, such as BoM (Bill of Materials), lead-time and inventory, as well as the basic calculation principles running behind commonly-used commercial production management software. To be able to master the course materials and the heavy-loaded project, I find it very useful to first form small teams (4–5 students) and define the role of each person in the team with a team chart before carrying out any assignment. In this way, students can understand the team work not only by splitting the homework and then working independently, but also by communicating efficiently and organising effectively. Several excellent teams I guided had always followed their team chart and organised their team work very well. Second, guided by the coach, intensive practice in automating data analysis and preparing as well as giving presentations in a limited time over a focused topic could help students master necessary skills for formally expressing questions and solutions in a concise way. These skills could help students from the mechanical engineering master a certain level of knowledge in business practice and therefore help them adapt to the life in an enterprise more easily. Last but not least, as a coach, it is important to induce open discussion in the coaching session to allow students to exchange thoughts about analytical methods, common mistakes and even innovative ideas together. Students can help each other understand mathematical formulations, which might be quickly given in the lectures, and learn about the theoretical background and related applications in the industry.

My main concerns about the coaching session are since the course would be evaluated for educational purposes, how to motivate students suffering both from a large workload and from complaints about difficult team work. The usual solution would be increasing both workloads of the coach and the team, but I found sometimes that small team-building activities, such as visiting companies related to their studied products in the team projects, could be very helpful to generate teams' common interests on the project. On the other hand, necessary face-to-face meetings between the team and the coach could also let most of the issues inside the team to become evident and open for discussion, thus leading to a solution before the situation escalates. A more open question about the course from the aspect of a coach is how production management method are going to evolve in the new era of the recently developed digital transformations of automated manufacturing, such as the concept of Industry 4.0 introduced by German government. Students were asking me if the methods learned from this course are going to be useful for industry in the future. The answer for this question could not be found easily from the course materials, but it is

somehow an interesting topic for the methodological development of production management in the near future. More insights or seminars could
be given by experienced coaches or even invited lecturers in the future for
the production management course.

Through the journey of coaching the course of production management
I learned excessively how to teach, mentor and enjoy the close relationship
between students and myself. Many of my students, I know, are actually
actively working in production management positions in large Swiss enterprises. I am sure that you will find more interesting topics during your
teaching and learning processes.

Yvonne Badulescu

I was a coach for the Production Management Masters course at EPFL
three times. The first time was during my final year in my Master's degree
after I had taken the course the previous year. I had a class of around
20 students which were split into 4 work groups. These coaching sessions
were very intense as the students were required to prepare a small part of
their case study to present. Sometimes I asked all of the groups to present,
and sometimes I would only choose one group, however it was necessary
that everyone came prepared to the class. I would like to start the course
with an overview of how that week's lectures fit into the big picture of
Production Management within a manufacturing firm. It helped having
taken the course a year before, as I remember which parts I had difficulty
understanding and those were the sections I would focus on during the
coaching sessions. The students were already high performing engineering
students who had excellent analytical skills but the majority had never
come across the type of topics that were discussed during this course, so
the subjects were quite novel and the coaching sessions brought a lot of
added value to their understanding.

The second year I was a coach, it was after working within a manufacturing firm as a junior supply chain engineer. The Production Management course gave me a great understanding of how production management
worked in the real world. I learned a lot in my new position and was very
pleased that I could bring that real-life knowledge to the classroom during
my coaching sessions. This new experience allowed me to provide examples
to the students of how the subjects they had just learnt fit into the bigger
picture. I could provide them with real examples which allowed them to

visualise the concepts they learnt in class. Similarly, with my third year of coaching, in which I could anticipate the type of questions the students had and prepare examples beforehand to help them understand.

All in all, it was a very fulfilling experience for me, so much so that I decided to go back into academia and pursue learning more about supply chain and production management and eventually helping more students learn about these topics.

Bibliography

Several academic works have inspired us in writing this book. Rather than referring them several times in each section, we prefer to list the main titles here below and take this opportunity to thanks their authors who inspired us all along this work. Some well-known online references were also used and are listed below.

Benton, W. C. (2014). *Supply Chain Focused Manufacturing Planning and Control* (CENGAGE Learning).

Business Dictionary (2017). `www.businessdictionary.com`.

Cambridge Dictionary (2017). `dictionary.cambridge.org`.

Investopedia Online Dictionary (2017). `www.investopedia.com`.

Jacobs, F. R. and Chase, R. (2017). *Operations and Supply Chain Management: The Core*, 4th edn. (McGraw-Hill).

NIST/SEMATECH (2013). *e-Handbook of Statistical Methods*, `www.itl.nist.gov/div898/handbook`. Last access on 1st October 2017.

The Free Encyclopedia (2017). `www.wikipedia.org`.

Vollmann, T., Berry, W., Whybark, D. C. and Jacobs, F. R. (2005). *Manufacturing Planning and Control for Supply Chain Management*, 5th edn. (McGraw-Hill).

Glossary

Aggregate Production Plan (AP) aggregated plan established usually on the level of a product family and taken into account future demand, forecasts, as well as the firm order book. The AP serves as an input to the MPS

Aggregate planning A process to develop tactical plans to support the firm's strategic plan. Aggregate planning results in aggregate production plan

Assemble-To-Order (ATO) production organisation that consists in running the downstream part of value adding chain, finish product assembly, on the basis of customer's orders and the upstream part on the basis of forecasts

batch a set of items to be supplied, produced, sold, delivered, etc used interchangeably with lot

batch size quantity of an item to be ordered, produced, delivered, etc. used interchangeably with lot size

Bill of Capacity (BoC) set of data providing the production load on each production center related to a given finished product

Bill of Material (BoM) an hierarchically organised list and/or graphical description of the constitutive items of a product

Bill of Operations A production Bill of Operations is a structure which describes manufacturing operation steps necessary to produce a product. It includes the definition of the work centre where the operation is to be carried out, as well as the sequence of steps that should be followed

buffer   A quantity of materials awaiting further processing. It can refer to raw materials, semifinished stores or hold points, or a work backlog that is purposely maintained behind a work centre

buffer inventory   A stock which contains buffer items

Cash Flow   net financial flow over a given time horizon; excludes all amortisations and provisions

coefficient of variation   a measure of the relive dispersion of a group of values; the variation coefficient is the quotient of the standard deviation by the mean

component   single part used in a sub-assembly or a finish product. Components are usually bought from suppliers

currency unit (cu.)   used for a general description of any national or internationally recognised currency unit such as $, EURO, CHF, etc.

delivery lead-time   time lag between order entry and delivery to the customer

market demand   market requirements for a given time scale (a period or a time horizon): can be for a finish product family, a finish product, as well as for spare parts

demand rate   demand per unit of time; often demand per planning period

dependent demand   demand of constitutive items, deduced from the independent demand; the demand of all items of the BoM is dependent, with the exception of the independent demand of finished products and spare parts

detailed planning   short term planning activities of production planning; medium level (level 2) of the hierarchical production planning approach direct cost cost that can be directly attributed to an operation, activity, without any distribution rule

economic order interval (EOI)   constant time interval between orders of quantity Qe in the case of constant demand rate

economic order quantity (EOQ) optimal order quantity obtained form a simple mathematical model, leading to minimising the total cost under certain assumptions; also known as the Wilson's EOQ model

economic order zone (EOZ) acceptable range of the order quantity around the optimal EOQ

finished product final product that is delivered to the customers

finished product family a coherent group of finished products that are characterised by strong technological similarities, in particular an important common part of their BoM

firm order customer order confirmed by some form of formal agreement such as a written order

fixed cost cost that does not vary with the production volume

forecast aggregation level item or item group used to establish the forecasts. Usually finish product, finish product family or turnover of the company

forecast horizon length of time over which forecasts are established (for example 18 months)

forecast reliability a measure of the "goodness of fit" of a forecasting process obtained by comparing the results of the forecast with actual data

forecasted demand for period t forecasted demand for a planning period (for example month, week)

general planning medium term planning activities of production planning; upper level (level 1) of the hierarchical production planning approach

gross requirement initial requirement in one period, not taking into account any on hand inventory or work in progress

hourly rate cost of one hour of an operation or an activity. It is obtained by dividing the total cost of the considered operation, activity by its the total duration. It a measure of the cost per unit time of a given operation or activity

independent demand   demand depending directly and solely on market requirements; an independent demand exists only for items sold on the market, i.e. finished products and spare parts

indirect cost   cost that cannot be attributed directly and exclusively to an operation, activity

inventory   sum of clearly identified items stored before, between or after value adding processes. Used also to designate the sum of the value of the stored items. Used also to designate the physical storing location and equipment. Used interchangeably with stock

inventory carrying cost   cost of keeping a given number of items in inventory for a given time span

inventory turnover ratio   ration between the value or the physical volume of the inventory output, disbursement of an item, item family or any given item group and the value, respectively the physical volume of the average inventory of the same items during a reference period (usually a year)

item   any physical object, from raw material to finish product, that is clear and uniquely defined and identified by an item code and/or number

item number   number and/or code used to uniquely identify an item

Just-In-Time (JIT)   operation management method aiming at producing the exact quantity, with the measured quality, exactly on time. JIT can further be regarded as an enterprise production management principle and is closely related to the Lean Manufacturing concept

launched order   production or purchase order in progress, i.e. that has been launched in the past (before the first period of the planning horizon)

launched order receipt   delivery of a launched order, at the beginning of a given period

lead-time   time required for a given activity or a series of activities. It is measured as the difference between the end time and the start time. In production, the lead-time depends on the production lot size and is therefore usually given for the average a most probable lot size

lot   a set of items to be supplied, produced, sold, delivered, etc used interchangeably with batch

lot size   quantity of an item to be ordered, produced, delivered, etc. used interchangeably with batch size

lot sizing policy   rule defining the lot size for a given item and a given operation

Make-To-Order (MTO)   production organisation that consists in running the entire value adding chain on the basis of customer's orders

Make-To-Stock (MTS)   production organisation that consists in running the entire value adding chain on the basis of forecasts and not customer's orders

Manufacturing Planning & Control (MPC)   encompasses all production management activities required for the planning and the execution of the production

Master Production Schedule (MPS)   plan established on the level 0 of the Bill of Material and taken into account future demand, forecasts, as well as the firm order book

Master Production Scheduling   production management activity consisting is establishing the Master Production Schedule

Material Requirement Planning (MRP)   production management procedure allowing to calculate the dependent demand of all constituting items of a finished product on the basis of its independent demand

mean forecast error, anchored at period t   mean value of the difference between forecasted and the actual demands for a given time horizon anchored at period t

need   requirement for any item for a given time horizon

net requirement   requirement in one period calculated from the gross requirement and taking into account possible on hand and work in progress ordering cost cost of placing an order or of launching a production order consisting of the administrative costs for launching the order, for its follow up, for receiving it and controlling it

on-hand inventory   volume of a given item that is actually available in inventory at the beginning of a planning process; i.e. that is available at the end of the immediate previous planning period. Synonym: on-hand balance

order book   list of the firm orders received from customers and not yet fulfilled order quantity order quantity for any purchasing or production order; not necessarily optimised

Part Period   Concept used in inventory management; one Part Period is equal to one item kept in stock during one planning period. The Part Period is proportional to the inventory carrying cost

planned order   production or purchase order defined in the plan but not yet executed

planned order receipt   delivery of a planned order, at the beginning of a given period

planned order release   launching proposal of a planned order, at the beginning of a given period

planning horizon   length of time over which the production planning process is applied (for example 18 months)

planning period   time bucket used in production planning, the planning period can be for example a day, a week, a month or a quarter depending on the objectives of the planning

production capacity   maximum amount of work that can be processed in a production unit (work centre, department, factory, etc.) within a given planning period

production centre   an organisational unit of the production: can be at any level between a local single machine and an aggregated level such as a whole factory

production lead-time   time lag required for a given operation and for an average lot size of a given article

production load   amount of work to be processed by a production unit (work centre, department, factory, etc.) in a specified planning period

production order a production order defines the quantity of a given item to be produced; the term "production order" is used also to designate the document containing the production order information

production planning anticipated hierarchical approach used to assure the availability of all necessary resources for the delivery of products to the market

production system a network of centres linked by material and information flows; its purpose is to deliver products to customers by adding value to raw material

projected available balance An inventory balance projected into the future. It is the running sum of on-hand inventory minus requirements plus scheduled receipts and planned orders

projected available inventory Synonym: projected available balance

reorder point a critical stock level that initiates the placement of a replenishment order when it is reached

replenishment time time between the placement of a replenishment order and the delivery of the corresponding item

requirement amount of one item to be produced, purchased, shipped, etc. in one period; depending on the calculation procedure, a requirement can be net or gross

resource profile set of data providing the production load on a given production centre over time for a given finished product routing set of information, specific to one item, indicating the series of operations that the item must go through; additionally, information about duration of each operation and many other specific information regarding for example the required tools are provided by the routing

safety lead-time time added to the actual lead-time of an operation in order to anticipate the delivery of an item into stock and thereby create an additional quantity in stock to cover up for unexpected events (increased demand, brake down of production, etc.)

safety stock Inventory held as buffer against mismatch between forecasted and actual consumption or demand, between expected and actual delivery time, and unforeseen emergencies. It is a level of extra stock that is maintained to mitigate the risk of stock-outs

service level   a measure of the degree of item delivery reliability

set-up   operations required before starting a production. It consists for example of changing a tool, adjusting a machine, cleaning the machine and changing the raw material, and so on. The set-up depends on the characteristics of the former and later production batch

stock   sum of clearly identified items stored before, between or after value adding processes. Used also to designate the sum of the value of the stored items. Used also to designate the physical storing location and equipment. Used interchangeably with inventory

stock level   amount of items in stock; a stock level can be a variable that indicates the current amount of items in stock or it can be a fixed number used as a management parameter (for example the level of the safety stock)

strategic planning   long term planning activities at the level of the enterprise

sub-assembly   constitutive module of a finish product that is obtained by the assembly of various items

Supply Chain   general term used to describe the chain of activities required from suppliers to final customers. It is often used but inappropriate terminology as the activities are rarely aligned in a linear way but rather form a complex network. Furthermore, a demand chain is also required in order provide the required information. Therefore one speaks also of the supply and demand chain. The author thinks that Value Adding Network is a more appropriate term

Supply Chain Management (SCM)   the process of planning and executing the operations of a value adding network as efficiently as possible. Supply Chain Management spans all movement and storage of raw materials, work-in-process and finished goods from point-of-origin to point-of-consumption. Supply Chain Management encompasses the planning and execution of all activities involved in procurement, production & assembly and distribution

time horizon time horizon considered for a given planning activity; typically 4, 6, 12, 18, 24 months

time phasing discretisation of the time scale into time buckets called periods

unit cost The cost of a single item, found by dividing the total applied costs for a given period or for a given operation by the number of items produced in that period or operation. The total cost associated with a particular volume of output divided by the number of items produced

Value-Adding Chain a specific case of a Value Adding Network characterised by a linear arrangement of the centres

Value-Adding Network (VAN) a network of centres (often called nodes) linked by material & information flows; its purpose is to add value to incoming material flows in order to assure an outgoing material flow with higher value

variable cost cost that varies with the production volume

work in process a set of physical objects that are undergoing a transformation through a value adding process; the exact status is often not precisely known as the process underway transform a start item into an end item. Used interchangeably with wear in progress

work in progress a set of physical objects that are undergoing a transformation through a value adding process; the exact status is often not precisely known as the process underway transform a start item into an end item. Used interchangeably with wear in process

Index